Taking Out
The Trash

Taking Out The Trash

EVERYDAY STORIES OF LIFE, LOSS,
AND LAUGHTER

Ros Hill

ibooks

ibooks

To
James W. Wheless, M.D.,

Thanks for showing me the importance of routine.
Not a week goes by when I don't roll the trash can out
to the curb and reflect on that.

Contents

Foreword
(How it all began)

S terling Archer Nesbitt was 7 months and 22 days old. I had just seen his picture in the local newspaper. Sadly, it was part of his obituary.

Unable to sleep, I read it many times over. I never knew him, yet there I was at 2:30AM, my eyes welling in an unexpected state of mourning. I was 47 years old, and felt like I had lost a best friend.

And how quickly it came—a visceral feeling—an unavoidable urge to reveal my thoughts regarding Sterling. I got a pen and paper, and began to write. So many emotions coursed through me as I paid homage to such a short life. I funneled my sadness into writing a story that was generated by tragic inspiration, completing the first draft in an hour. I never did go to sleep that night. Instead, I stayed up with Sterling until first light when I titled his story, "Sterling Spirit."

It was then that I realized I had a gift of being able to convey and express my perceptions of life through writing. A year later, I would serendipitously find myself in the living room of Sterling's parents' home, where I read them his story. It was no easy task as emotions quickly filled the air. There isn't, after all, a more devastating blow to a parent than to lose a child. When I finished, they shared something with me that truly lowered the weight of Sterling's loss into my heart: their tattoos.

Sterling's mother's tattoo is four inches above her belly button… the "momma spot" as she calls it. It's also the area that hurt the most when Sterling died. His dad's tattoo is on his chest, just above his heart. In both tattoos, symbols of Sterling's middle name, Archer, are evident with bows, arrows, and an archer. "Genuine" and "True" are written in the mother's tattoo which defines the name Sterling. I've always been intrigued by the thought process that goes into designing a tattoo. And while the artwork representing Sterling contains numerous symbols of his being, there was the one thing that made their tattoos powerfully different than almost any other tattoo I have ever seen… the ink contains Sterling's ashes.

Taking Out The Trash is a collection of how I see this amazing and unpredictable world. Not only does everyone have a story, but there are plenty to be found all around us: in the moment of discovering a tree, in the eye of an elk, in the drudgery of Monday, in the everlasting smile of a custodian, or in the act of taking out the trash. Within the sometimes vulnerable and fragile fabric of our lives, there also exists humor, inspiration, insight, and heartwarming and thought-provoking ideas that keep us captivated and moving forward.

In writing this book, that's exactly what I set out to do. The stories are a mix of non-fiction and fiction, though much of the fiction is based on real events. Some stories are accounts of people's lives. Some include fictitious portrayals to illustrate an opinion. Some are just my mind taking an idea for a spin, and seeing what becomes of it. But all are written to entertain and engage. If you find yourself laughing, crying, wishing, or wondering, then no worries…the book is doing its job.

Let Sterling be your first read, as he's got the lead-off position. Keep in mind that the spirit is a very powerful thing. You never know…he just might lead you to a life happily ever after.

—Ros Hill

Taking Out
The Trash

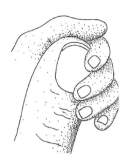

Sterling Spirit

I f you ever saw the smile of Sterling Archer Nesbitt, you would no doubt believe that his face captured every bit the magic of pure innocence. There was also a soft and quiet contemplation about him—a sort of weightless gaze that seemed to delight in his curiosity about all the things he saw. I never knew Sterling, nor did I ever meet him. I only saw a black and white picture of him in the newspaper—a thumbnail-sized photo of about a square inch for us to get a glimpse into his short, but beautiful life.

Sterling Archer Nesbitt was exactly 7 months and 22 days old when he died.

I have never known anyone that young, who has passed away that soon. Regardless, I can tell you that from the moment I saw him, Sterling had already left a mark on this world, well beyond that of the family and friends who loved him. There was something mesmerizing about his face being frozen in time in that photo. Looking at his picture, I couldn't help but wonder how his life might have been—not so much the places he would have seen, but rather the people he would have met. These are people he would have touched and changed. While he was never given that chance to make those connections, one thing is for sure: the spirit of Sterling is alive and will do its job to take care of what Sterling would have done.

While the impression he has made on me is quite real, I can't help but feel for his parents and his brother. In the obituary, there was a poem by W.H. Auden that ran alongside Sterling's photo. The last two stanzas read:

> *He was my North, my South, my East and my West,*
> *My working week and my Sunday rest.*
> *My noon, my midnight, my talk, my song:*
> *I thought that love would last forever:*
> *I was wrong.*

> *The stars are not wanted now; put out every one,*
> *Pack up the moon and dismantle the sun,*
> *Pour away the ocean and sweep up the woods;*
> *For nothing now can ever come to any good.*

When a gift like Sterling is snatched away from your cradling arms, and you have nothing but a heart of emptiness to fill the void, how does one cope? I have a good friend who, some forty years ago, lost her son, Jeff, to a brain aneurysm. He was 16 when he died, and our entire neighborhood loved him. We loved Jeff's character—his zest for life, and his simple, good nature. I was 7 years old at the time, but I still vividly remember the group of adults in the mother's living room. With heads down in disbelief, and tears dropping like rain, there was nothing but darkness to grasp. Even the collective comfort that was there to console the parents was having a difficult time making sense of anything. Though the intense grieving has passed, to this day, she still accidentally calls her other kids by his name.

I think what it all comes down to—writing these words—is hoping the families of these kids will see the ripple effect that their children have had, even if a life doesn't make it to a year. One more day. If that was all that was granted for a parent to be with their lost child, they would take it in a heartbeat. One more minute. One more second.

And that is all that I am asking for. One more day, every day, to keep remembering Sterling as someone who mattered—someone who, ironically, lived like there was no tomorrow. For anyone who refuses to live that way, remember the incredible boy named Sterling Archer Nesbitt. He just might lead you to a life happily ever after.

Super Tiny Little Bags
of Peanuts

Dear American Airlines:

I'm writing in hopes that you will mail me the super tiny little bag of peanuts that I did not receive on my recent flight from Texas to North Carolina. I realize these are hard times with your 2014 net profit of $942 million, but can I please have my super tiny little bag of peanuts? I'm not a mathematician, but here are some numbers I'd like to share and crunch with you:

124—the number of seats on the Airbus A319. All occupied.

410—the cost in U.S. dollars of my ticket.

8—the number of ice cubes served in my orange juice.

.5—the weight in ounces of a super tiny little bag of peanuts.

If all the passengers paid my ticket price, then American Airlines pocketed a healthy $50,840. Are you telling me that within that amount, you can't afford to serve us even one super tiny little bag of peanuts per passenger? How much can these peanuts really cost? 10 cents tops? And if that expense is really breaking you at the bank, then charge us a dime so you can at least break even. You could get really sneaky and hide the 10 cents in our ticket price. (Your flight to North Carolina will be $410.10)

Could it be your peanut expenses are so exorbitant because you buy premium peanuts that are exclusively grown atop some mountain in some remote region of the planet that it costs an arm and a leg to have them harvested and transported by exotic alpacas to a heavily, security-patrolled packaging and distribution center? Or can you not afford to serve super tiny little bags of peanuts because of their massive payload?

More math: 124 bags of peanuts (1 per passenger) = 62 ounces. Whoa!! Talk about messing with an aircraft's fuel economy! And the stress those super tiny little bags must put on the food & beverage trucks that deliver the peanuts to the planes. Just imagining that will blow your mind! Think about the wear and tear that the tires of those trucks must endure. No doubt, I'm sure all food truck operators are highly trained to detect low tire pressure and signs of impending tire failure.

I can certainly sympathize with your payload concerns. My orange juice had eight ice cubes. A weight of at least four times that of a super tiny little bag of peanuts. Multiply those ice cubes by the number of drinks served and we are looking at some pretty serious combined weight. An argument alone that puts to rest any discussion regarding whether or not American Airlines can handle peanut payload. The ice cubes have maxed out all complimentary food and beverage weight allowances.

A month before my flight to North Carolina, I flew from Texas to Michigan on Delta Airlines on a very similar sized airplane. And guess what? We ate like complimentary kings!

My conversation with the female flight attendant went pretty much like this:

FA: Sir, would you like a snack?

Me: Well, sure! What's cookin'?

FA: We have cookies, pretzels, and America's favorite: super tiny little bags of peanuts.

Me: Wow! A smorgasbord! I'll take a super tiny little bag of peanuts.

FA: Would you like more than one bag? Like two or three?

She had golden hair cascading like warm sunshine onto her shoulders. Her eyes were as blue as the waters of Grand Cayman. And she had a smile as happy as Christmas morning.

Me: Please, shower me with super tiny little bags of peanuts!!

The reality is that while Delta Airlines is successfully acquiring customer satisfaction, American is gambling on the hopes that their strategy of offering only complimentary drinks and ice cubes will appease its passengers.

To that, all I can say is: American Airlines, your head is truly stuck in the clouds. It's time to get grounded and reacquaint yourself with your passengers. You are merely one tiny little bag away from seeing the big picture.

Three years after writing this story, I flew from Austin, TX to Minneapolis, MN on American Airlines. And, to my surprise, what was kindly handed to me by the flight attendant was a super tiny little bag of peanuts!

Though I couldn't resist not including this story in the book (I mean, come on...it's a funny piece), the great peanut offering was proof that not only do miracles happen, but that there is change in the air.

Kryptonite

If you're looking for someone to go camping with, don't ask me. Because: A) I'll eat all the food, and B) if you ask me to start a fire with no matches or a lighter, then be prepared for one long, cold night.

Look, I'm a jock. I'll race you to that tree. I'll swim in a river against the current and get somewhere. Give me a rock and a target and I'll hit a bullseye. However, set me loose with a group of camping enthusiasts, and watch poetry in atrophy. Give me a rope and ask me to tie a knot to secure something, and I'll tie it so horribly wrong that the rope will look like a chaotic, frazzled wad of shoestring intertwined in a bird's nest.

This is pretty much how it plays out if I go camping...

The idiot in me agrees to go with four guys (only one of them I know) on a three-day rugged hike into an inhospitable region of dense wilderness where mosquitos and horse flies await to ambush me like a plague of possessed flying syringes. Their clothes and backpacks give me the impression they have each won a $5,000 shopping spree at REI. I arrive in cargo shorts, a t-shirt, and running shoes. My "backpack" is an Adidas drawstring sackpack containing an extra pair of socks, and an extra t-shirt. I also brought a sleeping bag and a one-man tent that I purchased at Target during their "Outdoors Combo Special" for $49.99. The weather forecast calls for a high of 72 degrees and a nighttime low of 52. A gentle breeze is out of the south at 5 mph. I don't bother to check the extended forecast. An imbecileian mistake.

And then I, and only I, am the chosen one asked to get a campfire going...

My buddy hands me a 4" broken piece of something. I look stupefied at this object, as if it's an artifact fallen from an alien spaceship. I really have no idea what I am looking at or what I'm supposed to do with it. It could be a petrified Snicker bar for all that I know. He sees the clueless look on my face and explains that it's a broken piece of a steel file, and I need to strike it against some quarts to create sparks to start the fire. All I have to do is find a rock with quartz. I truly believe I might be better off being asked to find a golden unicorn baking sugar cookies in the belly of a whale.

Not about to show any weakness in my complete lack of outdoor survival knowledge, I say, "I got this." Yeah, I got this like a stringless kite flying amok in the wind. As I put my head down and begin looking at rocks, I pick up a pebble not much larger than a gnat's brain, and actually consider its fire-generating possibilities. I scrape it over the piece of steel and, doing so, rake off part of a fingernail and lose the pebble. Good lord, I am doomed.

There's a river located a few hundred yards from where we've decided to set camp. Certainly I'll be able to find quartz there. But I have no idea what I am even looking for other than something that is similar to Kryptonite or has the appearance of sea salt magnified under an electron microscope. Doomed is an understatement.

The river flows strong, and is blessed with a fertile rocky shoreline. Thousands of rocks! For 20 minutes I scour this rock farm, but see nothing resembling quartz. Not a single one of them is calling my attention. Fifteen more minutes of rock combing and my attention shifts. I see that there are many rocks the size and shape of baseballs. I abandon my search for Kryptonite and begin seeking out a target. It's an old tree stump on the other side of the river. My very first throw lands a direct heavy thud in the middle of the stump. It bounces off and rolls into the river, as if in happy celebration of its impact. I challenge myself to a further target, and spot an elm tree a little further beyond the stump. I gather about ten prime baseball rocks and, within a minute, I miss with each throw. The competitive monster in me takes over and I begin throwing all types of rocks in rapid succession. Even a few cluster bombs of smaller ones. Faster and faster I throw, recklessly picking up more rocks and throwing them like a clumsy child. And then it happens…

KRYPTONITE!!

During my feverish rock harvest, my hands felt something with distinct ridge-like edges. It had a pinkish, semi-translucent appearance. What a great feeling when you know you're a complete camping failure, and then you excavate a major component for making fire. And how quickly that great feeling can vanish—like ice smothering an ember—when you realize, amongst those rocks you were throwing in rapid fire, you also sent flying a 4" piece of steel. The river being too wide and too strong to cross, I begin preparing my story for the guys… *"You won't believe the size of the bear that just chased me!! I had to drop everything and run!!"*

*   *   *

I woke up to first light, my toes seemingly frozen, and my body not faring too well either. A sharp northern wind blew in overnight and is knifing its way through the trees and straight into my shivering body. My sale item Target sleeping bag is about as insulated as Saran Wrap. In the middle of the night, restless sleep had me tossing and turning to where I uprooted the stakes anchoring my tiny tent. I basically looked like an ill-made polyester cocoon gone wrong. The smell of a campfire infiltrated every thread of my clothing. My bear story bore no believability since the last time a bear was spotted in these woods was…well, never. So I told them I must have mistaken the bear for a honey badger. They erupted in laughter. "Well, you may suck at camping, but you do have comedy going for you!"

Not long after that, one of the guys headed down to the river and came back two minutes later holding a large chunk of quartz. He gathered up some tufts of dry grass and some small twigs, picked an open area, pulled out an old worn steel knife, and began scraping the quartz very close to the grass. Moments later a few sparks appeared, and soon after that the grass caught fire. He looked at me and said, "Hey, keep your day job." I imagined commanding a pet honey badger to go rabid on his face, followed by a gang of gnarly trolls to cook him in a cauldron of boiling toad soup. Though the imagery is heavenly, it is nothing more than imagery, and so, he wins.

The good news is the camping trip piqued my interest in geology. I now have a quartz collection that sits upon my fireplace mantel, right above where a propane-generated fire burns brightly. And all at one flick of a switch!

I Can't Even Think That Little

When I think about the enormity of the universe and all that it contains—planets, stars, solar systems, and galaxies—and that, stars alone, there are too many to count in a lifetime, it becomes an impossible task to grasp that enormity. Try as I may, but all I'm left with are shards of a blown mind.

How contrasting it is to be sailing on a deep sea fishing boat, where there are no land marks in sight. Where I am eclipsed with one predominant thought: *I am tiny.* But that's only in comparison to the ocean, which on the scale of the universe is no larger than a mere microscopic fragment of an atom. As I wait for a fish to tug on my line, I realize that putting my diminutive size into perspective is so much of a chore, that I can't even think that little.

Within the moment of that thought, as I spin on a planet that never ceases to stop orbiting the sun, I measure myself on a scale that is so large, I can only describe its size as infinite, which leaves me unable to even think that big.

But think big I do. And sometimes too big of myself. I think big about big money. I think it's going to make a big difference in my life. And in my mind, that's a big deal. I think big about winning a running race. About winning a big argument. I say to someone challenging me: "Well, if you're so big, do it yourself!" I get a big ego over what I think are big accomplishments…*I mean, those were some pretty big weights I put on the bench press today.* And yet, the bigger I think, the less important

11

I reveal myself, and truly the smaller I become. Unless it involves thinking with big vision and doing things for others that will make a big deal.

Of course, thinking too little of myself can lead to little self-worth. If my confidence is too little, then there's little I can do for others. All it takes is a little determination and fortitude, and I can make a big difference on a little planet. Help a little elderly woman across the street. Give a little hug to someone in need. Pay a little bit bigger tip to a deserving waitress.

Somewhere between this yin and yang of big and little hangs a balance of good. It's a place where the two contrarians mutually benefit from each other. It's a place of alliance and understanding where the ego shrinks and the heart expands.

The enormity of the universe is incomprehensible. Its sheer size is beyond measurement, especially if it's infinite. But whether or not that is the case, is irrelevant.

In a world that seems larger than life, surprise someone today. A little effort can make a big difference.

The Bathtub

hen I was six years old, I could always gauge a successful bath by how furious my mom got. It wasn't my intention to send her into a hard boil, but things just ended up that way. I tried my best to contain the water within the walls of the bathtub, but sometimes the age of six can just get the worst of you. The image of her is still quite clear: a thick, tangled pile of dark brown hair—unkempt from a long day of house cleaning and cooking—strewn about like a nest of rattlesnakes. Her brow pushed down hard upon her fiery eyes blistering with agitation. I do not remember fingers clinched around a metal spatula, but rather hawk-like talons dripping with turkey gravy. And there she stood, towering just inside the doorway—a mythological creature—part Medusa, part gargoyle.

"WHAAAAT ARRRRE YOOOOU DOING!!!???"

I looked at the bath water covering the entire bathroom floor, fully permeating the throw rugs, and seeping into the hallway carpet. There was water running down from the mirror five feet away, broken glass next to the sink, and the strong smell of mint. Whatever sense of guilt had surfaced had just as quickly been dismissed, as I realized there had been a battle here. How was I possibly to blame? I looked at my green, plastic army men snipers, positioned on the sink's countertop, toilet tank, and atop the perimeter bathtub wall. About twenty of these snipers had fallen victim as casualties of war, and were bobbing up and down in the warm porcelain pond full of large, foamy mounds of Mr. Bubble.

Unbeknownst to my mother, beneath the soapy bubbles and darkened water ridden with dirt from a full day of playing, there lurked a sea beast (a.k.a. hand towel) intent on only one thing: to destroy each and every green sniper. This sea monster would erupt out of the water and unleash its mighty cotton tail, doing everything in its power to defeat the horrendous onslaught of enemy fire. Like a bullwhip, it lashed out at the snipers on the tub wall. Helplessly falling into the porcelain pond, the monster made sure they were sealed to their deaths by crashing down upon them as hard as possible. Over and over and over the monster repeated this thunderous impact, sending cataclysmic towers of water so powerful they splashed against the ceiling sky. Next, a raging roar echoed as the monster went into a full-body helicopter spin over the floor, thus wiping out an entire battalion of countertop snipers, including three toothbrushes, a soap dispenser, and shattering a glass bottle of mint-flavored Listerine. The monster then quickly retreated back to the tub, where it reconstituted its body with bathwater before repeating the same attack upon the division of soldiers firing from atop the toilet tank. No life would be spared.

And then the quiet.

A bathroom once occupied with heavily armed men, now stood silent in the wake of the aftermath. The monster, fully spent, retreated to the depths of the pond and laid hidden beneath the mounds of foamy bubbles—staying clear of the one force that could completely shut it down: my mother.

"WHAAAAT ARRRRE YOOOOU DOING!!!???"

Amongst this battlefield of fallen snipers who were either toppled onto the flooded floor or perished in the tub or, worse, plunged into the toilet bowl, I suddenly realized I was the lone survivor. While it's true I had been the omnipotent orchestrator, narrator, and participant of the battle, I found great pride in the fact that I had survived this devastation.

As for the snake-haired gargoyle that stood in the doorway,

breathing like a coal-fed furnace, I had only one chance of escaping her wrath. Without this one chance, I was sure to meet my end. I was sure to never return to school to tell the tale of the great sea monster. I was sure to join the dead snipers bobbing up and down in the porcelain pond.

And then I heard the footsteps. My one chance had arrived: my father.

"Well, looky here!" he said, in a jovial voice of excited discovery, "We got us a war zone! How's it going there lil' buddy!?"

I could not have sighed any longer or deeper. Grabbing a nearby bottle of shampoo, it was time to take my bath. And why not? After all, I had survived.

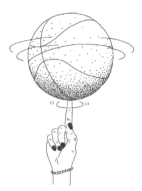

92 Years Young

Rouye Rush stopped aging when she was 72. She didn't die. She just stopped aging. It was as if her body and mind woke up one day and simply said, "To hell with it! Forget slowing down. Forget shuffling around all bent over. Forget losing muscle mass. And certainly forget losing memory and clear thinking." If you've ever been one of the lucky ones to meet Rouye, chances are there's no way you would ever deny the fact that she stopped aging at age 72.

But step into a gym with her and, like anyone else, you'll begin to wonder how is it even remotely possible that she is...

Excuse me, but where can I find Rouye Rush? Oh she's the one over there passing the basketball with her personal trainer. Yep, that's her— the one dribbling the ball between her legs. The one making the backwards bank-shot off the backboard. The one executing perfect behind-the-back passes. Good lord! How is it even remotely possible that she is...

Ladies & Gentlemen!! Step right up! Come witness the Main Event. The spec-tac-u-lar Rouye at work in the weight room! The single fact that she can effortlessly leg press 150 pounds without the slightest look of exertion should be proof enough that she is a miracle of nature! After all, how is it even remotely possible that she is...

...92 years old?

Envision a person her age, and most of us have no problem formulating the image of someone whom you would never trust behind the steering wheel of a car. Especially when you're a passenger.

But hop in the car with Rouye and watch her effortlessly and efficiently navigate a downtown area laden with construction. There's no need to cringe or worry about the route she chooses. For it is, after all, the route you would select. And so you sit in the passenger's seat, completely at ease with her navigational expertise. Every lane change, stop light, congested intersection, pot hole, iPod-wearing bicyclist…anything and everything that you might have to circumvent as you drive to your destination, she too does it with ease. A stereotypical 92 year-old she is not. It is as if there was a time when she just stopped aging.

The fact that she can do all of this (including shuttling people to and from a metropolitan airport, as well as hosting the annual Thanksgiving dinner for 34 people), it has a way of putting Rouye in a league of her own. She's like a pro athlete in that regard. Someone who has simply been blessed with a set of genetics that is incredible and uncommon.

Of course great genetics doesn't guarantee that you won't have to endure plenty of days of exhaustion. Such as the time she was en route for the Golden Gate bridge. Pretty much a typical day except for the fact that it was two days before Christmas and she was not only experiencing pregnancy contractions, but was traveling in a car with malfunctioning headlights. (Kind of a critical issue especially when you encounter a dark rainstorm near sunset.) There was no option but to drive back home and switch cars with a friend. Fearing Rouye might deliver the baby while traveling on the highway, her husband picked up speed in hopes to attract a policeman who might pull them over and then be convinced to give them an escort across the bridge to the hospital. Well, no cop in sight, he just pressed the pedal to the metal and went for it. Twenty minutes later he eventually made it in time. Stanley & Rouye Rush became the proud parents of newborn Dianne. Thinking back over the events of that evening and in particular what time of the year it was, Stanley said half-joking, half-serious, "How 'bout we name her Chris? You know, Chris, short for Christmas. Christmas Rush." Clever, but Rouye swiftly axed the idea.

There have been countless milestones throughout Rouye's life that she can recall in an instant. If you ask her about them she will describe the events in amazing detail. Tragedy, happiness, pain, the unexpected—the stuff which she has accumulated for nearly a century—she can tell you all. In 2009, she lost a daughter to kidney disease. It had been an on-going illness that eventually overcame her. "It shouldn't be that way," she says, "When a mother outlives her daughter." But it is what it is, and Rouye was left with no choice but to move on. Though she'll be the first to tell you that life is never easy, she'll also be the first to tell you that life is incredibly beautiful. You just never know what each day will offer. However, if after 92 years you happen to possess the gift of having a sound mind and body, then by all measures, count yourself lucky.

Perhaps if you ever get the privilege to talk to Rouye you might catch her on one of those days when she's at the gym, passing a basketball with her personal trainer or heaving a 10-pound medicine ball. Rest assured it'll be one of those humbling encounters when you'll walk away and want to share the moment with a friend, to claim bragging rights to having met a living person who, twenty years earlier, stopped aging at 72.

Hope

The Song

It all began with $85.00.

Paul: "Hello?"

Time Warner Cable: "Hi, this is Time Warner Cable. Is this Paul Tesh?"

Paul: "Yes it is. You can call me Paul."

TWC: "Mr. Tesh…Paul, we have not received a payment from you in two consecutive months. We will be stopping your service if not paid by Friday."

Paul: "Well, it's not exactly my fault. I blame it on a couple I never got to know while visiting Boston."

TWC: "Regardless, sir, if you don't pay by Friday, your service will be terminated."

Paul: "Perhaps you should listen to my story."

TWC: "Sir, I don't—"

He interrupted the representative, and told her to give him just a couple minutes to explain. She somewhat obliged and told him to go ahead.

Paul: "Three months ago my wife and I were in an Italian restaurant in the North End of Boston. While we were waiting on our order, I couldn't help but notice the number of people wearing Boston Bruins hockey jerseys. It was a sea of black and yellow. I asked our waitress if there was a game that night and where the stadium was. Before she could answer, a woman with her husband in a booth next to us explained that there had been an early afternoon game and told us the arena's location, mentioning it was the same venue where the Boston Celtics played. I had no idea they shared the same arena."

TWC: "Sir, I really need to—"

Cutting Time Warner off at the "Stop Your Service" pass, Paul continued.

Paul: "This will only take a minute. Please hear me out. So, the woman in the booth goes on to tell me about how they flew in from Pennsylvania just to see the game. We mentioned we were visiting from Texas to watch our daughter play basketball, and that we are loving every minute in Boston. And that was about it. A little later they finished their meal, and as they left the woman said, 'Enjoy your stay, and have a nice night.' "

TWC: "And that's why you can't pay your cable bill? Because some lady in Boston told you to have a nice night? Sir, I need to—"

Paul: "Ma'am, the reason I can't pay my bill is because I'm running out of money, and I've never felt happier! After that couple left the restaurant, their waiter came back to our table and said they had just paid for our meal, including the tip. They paid $85.00 for two people they had only talked to for, at most, three minutes."

TWC: "They paid for your meal?"

Paul: "Yes! I wanted to shake their hands, say thank you, hug them, and take them out to dinner the next night....something! But they left. Gone. Their identities forever unknown."

TWC: "What a bittersweet story. So generous, yet you could never offer your gratitude."

Paul: "Exactly."

TWC: "So, sir, not to sour your story, but your cable bill—I don't understand what your story has to do with not being able to pay your bill."

Paul: "It has everything to do with it. When I walked out of that restaurant, I couldn't get over how great an unexpected surprise can feel. Like a warm, hopeful blanket of generostiy had instantly been wrapped around me. You've heard of the term "pay it forward." Well, I've been paying it forward ever since.

TWC: "So much that you're literally running out of money?"

Paul: "Well, OK, not literally. But I am seriously wondering just how can I best spend my money? Do I want cable tv or do I want to brighten people's days?"

TWC: "Well, I know if you want cable, you better pay pretty soon or else—"

Paul: "Sorry to interrupt, but may I ask your name? Just your first name."

There was a pause on the line. A moment of uncertainty. Should she or should she not divulge her name? Was she thinking that he might be cornering her into something? Could this all be part of a master scheme he was brewing?

TWC: "Carol. My name is Carol."

Paul: "Hi, Carol. I'm Paul."

TWC: "I know you are," she said with a slight chuckle, "Paul who's about to lose his cable."

Paul: "Carol, I'm gonna pay the cable, don't worry. But can I ask you a question?"

Carol: "Go ahead."

Paul: "Have you ever heard a song that moves you so much, it lifts you up off your feet?"

Carol: "Absolutely. I know some songs that get me dancing like I'm hopping off the dance floor."

Paul: "No. I don't mean literally. I mean a song that *moves* you. Sinks itself so deeply into your heart and soul that you could swear you have discovered the purity of hope. So powerful is the feeling you just want to cry because never in your life have you ever experienced such an overwhelming sensation of happiness. It lifts you like never before."

There was a second pause. A few seconds before she spoke.

Carol: "Yes."

Paul: "What was that song?"

A third pause. Another moment of uncertainty? He could hear her inhaling slowly, then the gentle exhalation—the kind we take to compose ourselves. He knew this type of pause. It was musical, lifting. Carol was composing...

Carol: "The song that swept me off my feet and gave me permission to cry was 'Jennifer'."

Paul: "Jennifer? Never heard of it. What type of song is it?"

Carol was overcome with emotion. She was attempting to reply, but the words were having such a difficult time formulating. Then there was that familiar chuckle, pushing its way through the tears. Unmitigated happiness cloaked her, setting free her words.

Carol: "Jennifer. She's my daughter. She is my song. And never in my life did I ever expect music to be so beautiful."

And there Paul sat, on the other end of the line—caught in a moment that he never saw coming. Caught in a gulf of emotion that grabbed him like a tight fist ten times his size. This song, this Jennifer, this miracle whom he could only hope to one day meet. What an unexpected surprise.

But he paused. He was uncertain of whether to say it. To divulge or not to divulge.

Carol: "Mr. Tesh?"

Paul: "I'm here. Just give me a minute please."

A minute on the phone can seem like eternity.

Carol: "Mr. Tesh. Paul. You okay?"

He was composing. Trying to find the words. They were piled up in his brain, like a disorganized heap of logs that needed assistance to restore to order. But he dug deep and opened up the memory, releasing it into full exposure for Carol to hear.

Paul: "We lost our song before he was born. His name was Daniel."

Carol: "Oh, Paul, I'm so sorry."

Paul: "It's okay. Please, let me continue. We lost him at seven months. To this day, the doctors still have no idea what went wrong. One moment his little heart was beating, the next it settled into silence for eternity."

He took a deep breath that, if you were in the room next to him, you would have felt the anguish of its tiresome weight.

Paul: "Carol, it was four years ago. And, sure, to this day, as you can tell, it hurts. But my story is bittersweet as my wife is carrying our newest song. It's a she, and we have one month to go. Anything can happen. Anything. But, trust me, I have hope. I mean, why not? When that couple in Boston paid $85.00 for our dinner, it wasn't the amount that I was so impressed by. It was the generosity. It was the giving. It was the wonderment of surprise. And that's the stuff my wife and I hunger for. The surprise of how one song can lift you like never before. I've taken enough of your time, Carol. How much do I owe you?"

Carol: "Paul, your bill is covered. This one's on us."

Paul: "Carol, you don't need to—"

Carol: "I insist. End of discussion. Just pay it forward someday."

Paul: "And just how do you suggest I do that?"

Carol: "Oh, that's simple. Love your new song like it's all you'll ever have."

He said goodbye, and hung up the phone. Then, in a sudden defining moment of clarity and awe, and caught in a second gulf of emotion, he became fully aware of what the name of their new song would be.

Hope.

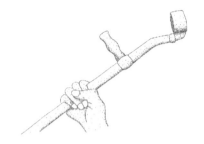

A Helping Hand

Spiders are not my most favorite creatures. In fact, the daddy long-legs spider---who's weight almost matches that of a postage stamp---is simply one such creature that I enjoy keeping my distance from. I can clearly remember a time when I was younger, taking a shower with a daddy long-legs walking up the wall next to me. Oh, the agony! You would think the only intentions that bug had was to jump out onto my face and bite me like a vampire. So, I whacked it off the wall with a big towel, sending it down the drain with ten minutes of continuous hot, steamy water. Afterwards, it dawned on me that maybe, just maybe, that was a slight overreaction.

True challenges are those that are seemingly insurmountable. They are of big issues, whether mental or physical. When you can face those challenges without fear, that is the measure of strength. When I was in 5th grade, I faced a challenge that came in the form of not just a classmate, but a girl. While she challenged me to an arm wrestling match, there was so much more to it that made me realize how small our problems are, and how we don't even have a clue about how to face the bigger ones (and I'm talking far beyond the horrifying threat of a single daddy long-legs spider). Inspiration comes in many forms. This one came in a lunchroom.

School lunchrooms packed with 5th graders are noisy, busy, bustling places. Food has a way of being projectiled at short, random intervals. Amongst that chaos, Sherry Nevius made her way to my table and asked a simple question: "Would you like to arm wrestle?"

Since when do zebras come out of the brush and ask lions if they wouldn't mind sharing some of their warthog carcass?

I looked at Sherry and said that she must be crazy. She looked at me and said she wasn't.

Word quickly spread throughout the lunchroom that the match was on. The sound of wooden chairs could be heard scraping over the linoleum floor as the kids backed themselves from their tables and made their way over to Sherry and me.

"Come on, Sherry, are you sure you want to go through with this?"

There was a short pause before she answered. But long enough for her to offer a slight smirk with raised eyebrows. "Are you?"

To a 5th grade boy, there is nothing worse than a girl who has nerves of steel. This was a challenge that was beyond any other. On the outside, I showed confidence and accepted the invitation. On the inside, my stomach was turning ugly knots. Still, I gritted my teeth---doing whatever I could to muster bravery. My friends gathered around me for support as I prepared to slay Sherry with an iron fist. The lunchroom was taking on the look of a "G" rated prison riot with harmless kids standing and chanting on tables and chairs. In my eyes, this was the match of the semester. The boys cheered my name; the girls, hers.

*   *   *

Two schools shared this packed lunchroom: Metcalf (grades K-8), and Fairchild, which was a school solely devoted to the mentally and physically challenged. Since kindergarten I had grown up with kids who were plagued with cognitive development disorders, cystic fibrosis, cerebral palsy, and multiple sclerosis. There were also the deaf and blind. Wheelchairs, crutches, walkers, walking sticks, protective helmets, and hearing aide devices were commonplace. Some of the Fairchild students were integrated into our classes at Metcalf. Sherry Nevius was one of those.

Since birth, she had dealt with cerebral palsy. She got around with the aid of some metal crutches that were braced just above her elbows.

The upside to Sherry's disability: she had arms as tough as climbing rope and a grip that was fiercely alien.

Sherry raised her arm to ninety degrees on the lunchroom table, and rolled her fingers in the air as if to say, "Game on."

In my mind the challenge was becoming insurmountable, because my pride was at stake. I planted my elbow on the table, locked hands with hers, took a breath, and then went for it.

We were deadlocked for what seemed like minutes. Kids were going nuts. Teachers and cafeteria workers were practically placing bets. Her grip was unbelievable. Slowly, ever so slowly, I felt my arm inch over hers. My wrist got to the point of curling even more, until I had her. Down to the table I laid Sherry Nevius's hand.

The challenge was behind me. I had slayed the dragon.

When you're in 5th grade and you win a difficult arm wrestling match (and it doesn't matter who you wrestle), you will walk through school for the rest of the week reliving that moment, that victory.

Today, I still relive that moment, but with a very different perspective. You see, 35 years later, I have located Sherry, and we stay in contact with each other, sharing whatever may be going on in our lives. In the years that have passed, she has not only acquired two college degrees, but has led a very self-sufficient and fulfilling life. She radiates the kind of positive energy that everyone should own. With all of the challenges that she has faced, she makes everyday living seem a breeze.

Yes, back in 5th grade I really never won the arm wrestling match, for it was Sherry who was chalking up victories right and left against all odds. It was Sherry who high-fived you at the end of the competition. It was Sherry who, at birth weighed half that of a five-pound bag of sugar, and not only spent her first six months in an incubator, but later had narrowly escaped being institutionalized.

And it was Sherry who, no matter how far she had to walk a crooked line in her cumbersome crutches, no matter how large the obstacle, she would always---and I mean always---find a way to win.

Two Minutes of Eternity

I set two alarms on my watch, three minutes apart, to wake me up. Almost without fail, the first alarm interrupts a dream. Typically I'm involved in some sort of bizarre impossibility, such as trying to fight off killer whales in a public swimming pool. Or were they gigantic penguins? I don't even know why I set the first alarm as I might as well be listening for a pin drop in a rock concert. At 7:10AM I sleep through the first alarm. At 7:13AM I stir to the distant annoying beeps of the second alarm. Why is it I have to summon every cylinder of motivation to get my fingers to generate enough energy to press the ALARM OFF button? I'd rather be saving the world in my sleep—fighting off those killer penguins with a kickboard.

The fact is I have to get up. But I might as well be a corpse sealed in a granite tomb.

The awareness of the morning creeps into view as my eyes try to open. It's that moment when I might lapse back into sleep for ten or twenty seconds. And when I awake again, there's a heavy brain fog that's cloaking the memory of my dream. The details are quickly fading. I was in a pool. Or was it a pond? And I was fighting something, but I can't recall what. Wait—it was a fish. A seal? Or was it a large black inner tube? My awakened conscious state acts as an anesthesia, erasing the recent events of my unconsciousness. The dream—and whatever the source of water was in that dream—instantly evaporates.

Two dogs lay beneath the covers: Domino, a rat terrier, and Sonic, a rat terrier dachshund mix. Sonic will sleep forever. Domino knows my alarms and prepares himself for the moment I swing my legs off the side of the bed to begin sitting up. That's the moment he will rise into his first stretch of the day. But that moment is a long, long, long time away. At least two minutes.

Two minutes of eternity.

I lay in bed and notice just how wonderful it feels to have no weight on my legs. How wonderful it feels not to be upright. How wonderful it feels to have arrived with a mind recharged. My senses fully heightened. It's when I think: *I need to write about this.* Within these two minutes, there is no rush, there are no deadlines, and there is no stress. Cocooned in a swirl of bed sheets and a blanket, I do more than just hear the birds outside my window—I *listen* to them. To the busy man on the street, birds are nothing more than producers of the same pestilent noise repeated over and over. But the busy man is missing it, for he is the one out of tune. He has no idea of the complexity of their *communication*. And so he shuffles past the trees, and crosses the street before entering a building where he is irritably late for a meeting. An hour prior, this man overslept his alarm clock and arose in a mess of hurried agitation. Somewhere in there, if he were lucky, he had at best two seconds of eternity. At best.

My time is up. My two minutes have ended. I know exactly what needs to be done in order to leave the house on time. As I swing my legs out of the bed, Domino pokes his head out into the open, then rises into his ritual stretch. Simultaneously, I lean into him and press my face against his soft neck, while slipping my hand under the covers to feel Sonic's belly. There's a warmth there that never fails to reassure me that I am truly connected to these animals. It's a communication that is ours and speaks volumes.

And then the epiphany hits: I'm learning to extend my two minutes.

Taking Out The Trash

September 11, 2001. Houston, Texas.

As I make my way down the stairs to the hotel lobby, I have no idea that this day is already making history.

I am in a bit of a rush, trying to make it to the hospital in time. My daughter, Brookney, is at Hermann Memorial Hospital where, beneath her scalp and placed over her brain's left hemisphere, is a grid of 120 electrodes. The wires from the electrodes are fed out through the incision in her scalp, and are bound together in a long, narrow cotton wrap that snakes its way to an EEG machine to record her brain wavelengths. She has been hooked up to this EEG for five consecutive days. It has been monitoring her brain twenty-four hours a day. She has epilepsy, and the EEG is used to help locate where her seizures originate. By reducing her dosage of medicine, and thus lowering her seizure threshold, she has given the doctors five seizures to study. The results are good: they have located the seizure focal point, allowing for a surgery that will involve the removal of a small portion of her left hemisphere, eliminating or greatly reducing her seizure activity. Her surgery will be performed on September 13th.

As I pass through the breakfast area of the hotel, I immediately sense an eerie feeling as everyone in the room is staring at the television. I look up at the TV and notice one of the Twin Towers is billowing with smoke. The network anchor people seem speculative as they mention a possible airplane that hit the building. And then, the scene that was so completely horrifying, a jet airliner quickly approaches the second Tower, knifing into it, then immediately bursting into a ball of fire as an explosion of debris erupts out the other side of the building.

The doctors make their rounds to speak to patients and parents in the mornings. My wife and I took turns sleeping in Brookney's hospital room and the hotel. I am in a rush simply because I want to be able to catch the doctor and see what new information he might have. As I leave the hotel and drive to the hospital, two questions occupy my mind for the doctor: With the turmoil our country has immediately been thrown into, will the surgery go on? (We had waited over a year to get to this point.) And, if so, how will you be able to focus?

The events of 9/11 consumed the entire hospital that day. Doctors, nurses, patients, parents, janitors, cafeteria workers, and security personnel hardly budged from the TVs. While my wife and I were no exception, we were in disbelief that it was all happening so close to our daughter's surgical date. It was a surgery that could positively alter the course of her life forever. For seven years she had been battling seizures. Sometimes up to fifteen in a day. We had our share of 9-1-1 calls to the house, and of seizures lasting over ten minutes. We had gone through nine different medicines, none of them controlling her condition. Her chance of growing out of the seizures was 2%. Her chance of the epilepsy being controlled by medication was 5%. The surgery was her last great hope, and two commercial airliners had just spoiled the day.

When that thought occurred to me---about how my life was now interrupted, about how my plans were just rerouted---it didn't take long for the questioning of selfishness to arise. I asked myself, *Is this right for me to feel cheated that my daughter's surgery might be postponed or difficult to perform now that the Twin Towers had collapsed?* From birthday parties to funerals, every single planned event across America was affected. Perhaps it was time I put our daughter's situation into perspective. While, yes, her surgery was crucial, it was not life threatening. New York City's problem was.

Though Houston was sunny that day, it was so very, very dark. But nothing like NYC. I had stayed there several times for business trips, and loved the city passionately. I was 1900 miles away from the towers, and I had felt them fall. I cried for them and I cried for Brookney. The future was uncertain in both directions. What I needed more than anything was hope.

It came in the form of the most profound and simplistic statement I have ever heard, much of which was due to its connection to the circumstances of that day. It was, literally, garbage.

When our doctor entered the hospital room that morning, he mentioned that the surgery was still on schedule, regardless of the state of the union. My reply to that was to the point, "But are you going to be able to give Brookney your complete attention, with no distractions?" I didn't mean to cast doubt on our doctor, and under normal circumstances the question would never have surfaced, but the circumstances were not normal. He understood my reason for concern and gave the reply that I shall never forget. He said, "This morning my wife asked me to take out the trash, and I did."

"Huh?" I responded.

"The trash," he repeated, "I always take out the trash. It's one of the duties of my weekly routine. A small one for sure, but one that if left neglected can have a disrupting effect on everyday living. Operating on children with epilepsy is another one of my duties. I know that I can't stop skyscrapers from falling down, but I can help improve the lives of children. We have to keep things moving forward. We have to take out the trash."

Not in my wildest dreams would I have ever imagined that a highly respected pediatric epileptologist would convince me that the reason I should feel comfortable with him performing brain surgery on my daughter, two days after 9/11, was because on September 11th he took his trash out to the curb.

By way of his explanation, not only had he offered me profound insight, but more importantly, hope.

The Window

He had a window next to his bed, with a view of the snowy woods. It was nighttime now, so all he saw was the reflection of his lighted room. But if he focused long enough, he could see through the reflection and catch movement in the dark. Bare tree branches moving erratically in the cold wind, knocking into each other as if quarreling, as if their dormancy had irritably come to life. If he could touch that window, the raw cold of the pane would shoot through his palms, sending a shiver through his body. However, the heavily wrapped bandages on his hands prevented such sensation. A nurse poked her head in the doorway and asked if he needed anything. Staring outside, he asked her to turn off the lights.

*   *   *

Early that morning the TV had been on, but it wasn't long before he realized it was nothing more than background noise. Sports, news, and entertainment channels became disinteresting. At his request, the nurse silenced the TV. And that was when he looked outside at the woods. That was when his mind went clear of thoughts, as if disengaged from everything, except for observing and absorbing the stark view of the trees against the snow. The overcast gray sky. The black birds momentarily perching themselves as they hopped branch to branch. The sharp wind carrying new snow. This interest of his, taking in the view of the woods, but more so the interest—where had it been? When was the last time he had been awed by nature?

It was before he left for college. In fact, it was before high school. And there was a window. The memory was vivid: in the living room, watching a heavy downpour soak his neighborhood. As a roll of continuous thunder vibrated china dishes stacked on a nearby kitchen shelf, one shattering strike of lightning daggered magnificent bolts of energy into his front yard. The thunder that immediately followed shook the house with deep bravado, in an apparent attempt to move those dishes over the edge. His eyes burst open wide at the perilous proximity of the strike. What if, seconds before, he had dared himself to run to the mailbox and back? It wouldn't be his first dare. He'd been foolish before in thunderstorms, running horrified with fear, but also with a confidence that he was going to return alive. But what if, this time, one electric tentacle from the bolt had flashed out and hit him? This view out the window would be no more. A second close strike hit a transformer atop a nearby telephone pole, emitting sparks, and severing one of the wires, sending it whipping into the air. The power in the house went out. He stood there, mesmerized by what he could not take his eyes away from. In his hospital bed, reflecting on that memory as he now looked out his dark window, he thought about his bandaged hands and the silent TV. His eyes were fully engaged in what mattered, what was real. And to this he had only one thing to thank: the accident.

He had been working the grill at a local diner, flipping burgers during a slow part of the afternoon. When things died down, he had the spatula going in one hand, and a cell phone in the other. As usual, texting, Twitter, Snapchat, and Instagram were the order of the day: Check the phone upon waking up. On the john, on the phone. Throw on some clothes, then on the phone during breakfast. Out the door and off to the university he starts walking. With head down and fingers flying over the keyboard, he navigates through a busy sidewalk full of other students—all of them, honed in on their phones and circumventing one another with peripheral vision. At a stop light, he finds himself stalled within a group. And there they stand, adjoined in conformity with what would appear to be a prayer session. This peaceful, reverent sight gives the impression that this gathering is showing solemn respect to some deserving person needing to be in their thoughts. But that is hardly the case, as upon closer inspection, there are hundreds of fingers tapping their touch screens—texting, tweeting, and snapping away. No quiet devotion going on here. Just quiet.

The world around them passes by: a blue whale painted on the full length of a garbage truck; a worker on the back of the truck, smiling as he waves to a father and son who are repeatedly kicking a rock along the sidewalk; a V-formation of geese flying overhead; and a squirrel narrowly escaping death as it dodges in and out of traffic to cross the street. Every fleeting moment worth being captured. For those habitually wearing earbuds, the sounds of the morning are muted or cancelled out. Wind chimes on a front porch, a flag flapping in the breeze, and the chaotic chatter of clicking, caws, and coos of a tree full of birds. Smells too are given partial notice. Fresh bread from the corner bakery, and someone somewhere, with a window open, cooking bacon for breakfast. Day after day, the same route, the same routine, the same loss of sensation. All traded for technology. While they are indeed connected, they are also, without question, disconnected.

It's 2:30pm and the lunch hour rush is over. Work on the grill is slow with only occasional orders coming in. He's in the mood to post a comical video of himself in a sleep state standing over the empty grill. He props the phone up on a shelf, and begins recording. The grill's flat, metal cooking surface is searing hot at 400 degrees. Five seconds into his video a co-worker, carrying large empty boxes to the trash, bumps his back. And that's all it takes to make him lurch forward, and extend his arms to prevent his chest and face from hitting the grill. Against the scorching metal surface he plants his hands to break his fall. His full weight pressing directly into 400 unforgiving degrees.

His horrifying cry is the last sound heard before his body slumps, passing out onto the floor.

* * *

That day, in the hospital, as the sun was setting, he caught a glimpse of something moving amongst the trees. The crisscrossing of the tree's shadows played with his eyes, but he was certain he had seen it. And then, as if a reward for his patience, the fox appeared. It predatorily creeped over the shadows, before pausing with its head cocked and ears erect in the homing position. In one quick, explosive lift-off, it arched its body into the air, allowing it to nose-dive into the snow. Moments later, the fox surfaced with a field mouse in its jaws. How quickly it happened, how quickly it ended. The fox was gone, and the forest was left as it was, with tree branches moving erratically in the biting, cold wind.

When was the last time he had taken the time to look at something so seemingly ordinary? A view of the woods was offering him an endless supply of live footage. One window had done it all. No keyboard, video, sharing, liking, or posting required. All he had to do was keep his head up.

And then the realization: his accident—painful as it was—had, literally, opened his eyes.

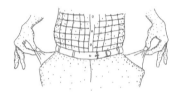

Congratulations!
You're Broke!

After you've purchased a car, why is it that nearly everyone in the dealership has to shake your hand and tell you "Congratulations!!"? Isn't it strange that you just gave them thirty-grand and you're the one responding, "Thank you."?

Something's just not quite right.

You've worked hard for your money. It used to be secure in a bank, but now you've drained your savings and have forked it over to us. Congratulations!

You get to pay us interest till it makes you sick. Congratulations!

Your brand new car will lose $2,000 - $4,000 the moment it's driven off the lot. Congratulations!

You get to pay for a vehicle registration fee, title fee, license fee, documentation fee, compliance fee, emissions testing fee, and advertising fee (though it wouldn't be surprising if a complimentary coffee fee, handshake greeting fee, test drive fee, and bathroom usage fee were tagged on as well). Regardless, congratulations!

Don't forget that extended warranty. Pay up! And congratulations!!

Best of all: From the moment you arrived, our commissioned sales vultures did everything in their power to corner you into an uncomfortable pressured situation so grossly laden with industry-wide deceptions, that if you didn't commit to buying on the spot, then your car's Limited-One-Time-Only-Like-This-Is-It offer would forever haunt your poor decision to pass up on the deal of a lifetime. Ah yes, the unenjoyable car buying experience that ate up half your day. Well, guess what? We got your money! Congratulations!

Why is it the high-dollar purchases hold the honors to a congratulations? Car, airplane, and boat dealers are all, well, in the same boat. And, unfortunately, the word congratulations *sounds* right. We've grown accustomed to it. Those industries have wielded their magical psychological tactics to figure out a way to make the incorrect usage of the word, correct. With other businesses, using congratulations after a purchase just sounds weird: *Congratulations on buying a brand new hammer! Congratulations on your haircut! You just paid us a $60.00 co-pay for your medical exam…congratulations!*

We should be thankful that businesses, from which less costly purchases are made, don't suck us into a backwards congratulations. Imagine your local grocery store…

Whoa! You purchased a box of cereal! Congratulations! And is that a pack of cotton balls? A sincere double congratulations!!

So that people feel good about their purchases, the grocery industry could apply similar "You've got to be kidding me!" car industry costs to their customers. All to ensure an even more spirited congratulations…

Aisle 7 Sales Professional: "Ma'am—that box of cereal—if times are tough, we can make it very affordable. Instead of paying $3.37 full price today, we can finance it at a low 2.5% interest rate for 12 monthly payments of only $0.29. All you need to do to apply is fill out the 53-page application form with any of our more-than-friendly cashiers.

More-Than-Friendly Cashier: "Here are a couple of pens ma'am, in case you run out of ink filling out the 53-page Agony Application. When you're finished, I'll be happy to process you after the man who's on page 28, applying to finance his apple. Oh, and remember, we can't guarantee total money-back of product coverage. While you do have a top-to-bottom of cereal box warranty, it doesn't cover Acts of Evil. Such as, if upon exiting the store, you were robbed at gun-point for your Raisin Bran. Our Extended Warranty Against Evil will guarantee a 100% money-back refund. Evil is all around us. Pit bulls, scud missiles, utility bills, and, of course—you knew this one was coming—cereal killers plague our streets.

Grocery Store Manager (extending hand): "Ma'am, I would like to be the first to congratulate you for being the proud owner of a financed box of cereal. Looks like you got quite a beauty there—fully loaded interior of sun-dried raisins, all packed inside one classy Frost Pearl and Glossy Purple exterior. I see you purchased the warranty against Evil. Smart choice. There's a heavily-tattooed man outside our store holding a carton of milk, a spoon, and an empty bowl. Chances are you're on his radar. But no worries…you are fully covered! That's not just a box of breakfast in your hands. That's an investment! And now that we have your money, well…CONGRATULATIONS!!"

Yes, the hearty congratulations from the car dealers needs to stop. It's time they showed their appreciation for your money. It's time they acknowledge that you practically had to rob a bank to be able to make the purchase.

And the day they can tell their buyers, "Thank you!" will be the day their buyers can offer them a firm handshake and say, "Congratulations!"

The Smile of Connie Cabello

You could write a laundry list of all the things my Uncle Ike was associated with pertaining to the medical industry. He was Vice Chancellor for Health Affairs at Vanderbilt University, had been the CEO of Duke Hospital at Duke University, and was president of the International Society of Nephrology. He lived a very comfortable life that allowed him to travel the world. He was one of the privileged few who flew at 1,334 mph in the supersonic Concorde jet from New York City to Paris in 3 1/2 hours.

He would eventually buy a nice boat for him and his wife to enjoy the waters of Naples, Florida. Time to simply get away. Of course, it was dwarfed by his friend's yacht. The same friend who would donate millions of dollars to Vanderbilt. Uncle Ike knew a lot of people whose financial holdings were very well off, and he too was fortunate to enjoy an affluent lifestyle. All of these people, including Ike, worked hard for what they earned. But if I had to tell you what his greatest success was, I wouldn't hesitate to say it was his ability to stay humble.

It was near the end of his life when I found myself sitting with him in his living room in Nashville. He had taken on a stubborn and rare form of lung disease. His house was loaded with massive oxygen tanks. He mentioned how he'd been wined and dined all over the planet. He talked about many of his travels and the various dignitaries he had met. Yet amongst all the wealth and important people that he had encountered, he came to find there was one group of people that he was particularly fond of. And that was the custodians. He said, "They are real people. They tell it like it is. They aren't ashamed of their jobs, and they're proud of themselves."

Uncle Ike paused for just a moment, then smiled as he shifted into his classic dry humor tone, "But the real reason I've gotten to know the custodians is because they have the keys to open every door on campus."

As I laughed, I couldn't stop thinking about a similar admiration I had experienced some fifteen years earlier—that of a short, bubbly Hispanic woman in Seguin, Texas.

* * *

Connie Cabello was a custodian. She worked at the radio station where I produced commercials and was a disc jockey. I wasn't the most skilled DJ, as I can recall numerous times I would leave the studio to go chat in the lobby with a record playing, only to forget that the record was playing. It didn't take but the duration of the song until I heard over the in-house speakers the sound of the turntable needle playing nothing but unrecorded vinyl.

Seguin is a small town where many of the citizens had names of German and Czech descent. I, of course, did a brilliant job of butchering their pronunciations—managing to screw up during the most opportune times. Like obituaries. I mean, seriously, here I was announcing their last great farewell on the airwaves and what do I do, but pronounce their names like a preschooler being asked to say "antidisestablishmentarianism". The phones rang off the wall as if I had butchered an American eagle. Reading the daily obituaries became a mind-shuddering experience. *Don't screw up! Don't screw up! Don't screw up!* That was the mantra that incessantly played throughout my mind as I waited for my microphone to go "On Air". And, of course, I'd screw up.

It seemed that every time I stumbled across a vocal blunder, Connie Cabello was there to throw me a smile. And it was that first smile I caught that I forever put in my pocket. Like the first dollar exchanged in a new business's first sale—mounted on the wall in a framed display. To this day, her smile beaming through that studio window is as new as the first time I saw it.

She quickly became that one person who I looked forward to seeing when I went to work. When I did the midnight shift, she'd stop by after having had a little too much to drink while dancing the night away at the local Hispanic dance hall. I was basically running the FM country station on auto-pilot as all the songs were taped. No more vinyl that I had to cue up and screw up. Everything ran through a computer playlist. All I had to do was watch the monitor, and pull wired news copy to read at the top of the hour. It was a sort of babysitter job that allowed me one great luxury: to hang out with Connie.

If we weren't laughing, we were digging up anything to laugh about. She introduced me to all the latest Tejano music and, of course, Mexican food. We began cooking for each other, sharing recipes on Saturday nights. I, being the white boy, would bring her spaghetti. She'd cook me her homemade pork-stuffed tamales warmly wrapped in corn husks that basically blew my socks off. Soon I said to hell with spaghetti, and became addicted to her Mexican treats.

One night Connie stopped by the station with just a few tamales, and told me she was going to stop eating them, that she needed to lose weight. She noticed that I ate a lot of salads, and asked if they would help her shed the pounds. We had a long talk that night about weight and healthy eating. Her excess weight was (to coin a phrase) getting under her skin. She had had enough, and wanted a change. Connie realized I was someone she could confide in, someone she could trust to share her frustrations with.

A few years later, I stopped working at the radio station. I had caught the travel bug. I was single with no ties, and so I boarded a plane and went backpacking throughout South Africa, Zimbabwe, and Namibia. I was half the globe away from Connie, but she would still pop into my head, even at the oddest times: going for a run in a safari base camp, fishing on the Zambezi River, awestruck at Victoria Falls, or standing at the very tip of Good Hope to watch the Atlantic and Pacific oceans collide.

As the years passed, Connie was always someone who I would call periodically. She wanted to know all the details of my family. She was highly inquisitive. If you didn't have a question for her, she'd endlessly fire them at you. I wrote her Christmas holiday letters, about anything and everything, often enclosed with family photos. Unable to read English, she had her daughter read them to her. She made a few trips to my house where she'd stay well into the night, laughing the majority of the time. She was approaching her seventies, but her energy level didn't indicate any such aging. She came over for a couple of Thanksgivings, always arriving with plenty of her prized homemade tamales.

Life got busier, especially with our kids being highly involved in youth sports. Everything exponentially exploded into back-to-back full days and weeks, and for that matter years. But Connie was still merely a phone call away. The excitement in her voice rose skyward when she heard me on the other end. Half of it was in Spanish, which meant I didn't understand half of what she was saying, but I fully *felt* all that she was saying. Her sincere voice—it had a way of settling softly into your heart.

The day arrived when we received a call from one of her daughters. Connie had passed away. The warm and ebullient gift named Connie had expired, but only in its human form. I'm pretty certain the magic of Connie is still circling this planet in some form or fashion.

The entire drive to the funeral home in Seguin, I kept telling myself: *I can handle this.* The parking lot was crowded. A lot of people had come to offer their condolences. *I can handle this.*

As I entered the funeral home, one thing was immediately evident: I was the only white person. And at 6'4, I probably appeared even whiter. The looks on their faces said: *Certainly you have the wrong place.* A woman approached me and said, "Excuse me, may I help you?"

"Yes, I'm here for—" I looked at her, and stopped mid-sentence.

I could see it…her eyes. In fact, her voice…remnants of Connie were addressing me. This Hispanic woman had a familiar friendliness about her as well. And how familiar it felt. "Yes," I said, "I'm here for Connie Cabello."

"And you are?"

"Ros."

I'm not sure I could have measured the fragment of time that passed from when I said my name to the time I saw the first tear fall from her eyes. And in that sudden wave of emotion, she was already holding my hand. Her chin quivered just before she released a trail of tears. We were both in a place neither of us had anticipated. She was one of Connie's daughters. "You're…Ros?" she said.

"Yes, ma'am."

"Ros," she said, "You—" She was struggling to talk, her throat gripped tightly with emotion. She took a deep breath, collected herself, then continued… "Ros, you were all my mother talked about. I mean she couldn't stop talking about Ros. You were her magic."

She guided me towards the main gathering of people. "Look," she said to them, "It's Ros!"

My name quickly circled the room. Hands extended towards me from all directions. Hugs from people I had never met. A reverent blanket of warmth filled the air. But I was a bit taken aback by all the attention. Sure, I knew Connie, but we all knew Connie.

I met the entire family and Connie's closest friends. And each time I made an attempt to talk, the words just never made it out. I knew I had impacted Connie's life, but never to such a degree that I would be rendered unable to speak. I had no idea how much I had influenced her life. Her daughter told me that after I would call her, she'd go to her collection of family Christmas photos that I'd sent over the years, and just smile. She couldn't read a lick of English, but when her daughter read her my letters, she shut out the world and permanently tucked my words inside her heart.

I'll never forget being in that room. I'll never forget the sudden and unexpected pang of regret that pierced my heart. What I would have given to have one last minute with Connie—to thank her for allowing me into her life. I wanted to give Connie all the credit in the world for bringing those warm tamales to the radio station. She didn't have to do it, but she did because she was a giver. I wanted to thank her for being the greatest audience of one on the other side of that studio window as I comically danced for her to cheesy country songs. Give me one more minute and I'd tell her how magnificent a sight it is to see two oceans clash at the very tip of Africa—a moment where I held her safe in my memory.

Referring to my Uncle Ike as he would say of the custodians of the world: In addition to having all the keys to the radio station, Connie never relied on wealth to give her value, and she was not ashamed of her job. She did, however, rely on one thing that never failed to succeed: her smile.

Connie…wherever you are…I've still got that first smile you gave me, tucked away in my pocket. I take it out now and then to remind me of what a difference you made in my life. And you know what?

I can handle this.

Thank You, Sammy Hagar

If someone were to have offered me $100 not to have a two-minute conversation with a woman whom I'd never met before, I would've turned it down in a heartbeat. A $500 offer? Getting up there, but I would've turned it down as well. Though chances are I'll never see her again, you can still keep your money.

She was a stocky woman behind me in a grocery store check-out line. Next to her was a girl about 13 years old. The woman, in her mid-50s, was hunched over the handle of her grocery cart in such a manner it looked as though she might have been giving her back a break. It was 9:30PM, and she had that end-of-a-long-day look—her face drab and expressionless. Her entire body just waiting to get home, heat up a frozen pizza, then collapse on the sofa. No need to prepare for bed. Just drift into sleep. In a moment of wrongful judgment, I actually thought: *Has her life always been this way?*

A couple in front of me paid for their groceries, then left. As I took the position in front of the credit card terminal, and the cashier began to scan my items, something happened that completely changed the scene.

A song began to play.

And as it played, a delay with the cashier occurred—a malfunction with his register. The delay took about a minute for him to fix. When I look back at this moment, I wonder if it's even remotely possible that this malfunction was more than just a coincidence. That it happened for a reason. Because without that extra one minute, I'm confident the ensuing magic would not have happened...

As the cashier tinkered with his register, the song could be heard throughout the store's sound system. I noticed the woman and the young girl began tapping their feet. Moments later they both began to quietly sing the song's chorus:

How do I know when it's love?
I can't tell you, but it lasts forever.
How do you know when it's love?
It's just something you feel together.
When it's love

"Good ol' Sammy Hagar," said the woman to the girl. "Or was this *Van Halen*?"

"It's Sammy Hagar with *Van Halen*," I interjected. "This is from their *OU812* album."

This woman with the presumed aching back, and long, tiresome day, and who lacked enthusiasm—she lit up a smile too big to be measured. "Of course it is!" she said, energetically. "You're right! This is *OU812*, and it was recorded at Studio 5150."

"You know about 5150?" I said, completely surprised.

The woman throws her head back, laughing with astounding joy. She is an absolute bundle of happy warmth. When was the last time I saw a smile this exuberant? When was the last time I missed the mark by so much, judging someone's state of being?

"Who do you take me for?" she laughs. "I grew up with this music. Big Sammy Hagar fan. My daughter here—she had no choice...it's all I listen to."

I asked her if she was aware of the group *Montrose* that preceded *Van Halen*. I think her laugh doubled in volume.

"*Montrose*!? You are too much!" she said. "Of course I am! Sammy

Hagar sang for them. Songs like "Space Station #5" and "Bad Motor Scooter". She was now laughing uproariously. "This is way too much!"

We are both caught in the moment. Smiling, laughing, and enjoying stumbling over a shared interest that, in itself, has miraculously and invitingly arrived with open arms.

Her daughter continues to tap her feet. Her hand slaps gently against her hip in sync with the song's beat. Her genetic coding is imprinted with an obvious character trait passed down from her mother: a priceless smile that snatches your attention and elevates you to a higher dance. Her eyes are nearly shut as she continues to sing:

> *You look at every face in a crowd*
> *Some shine and some keep you guessin'*
> *Waiting for someone to come into focus*
> *Teach you your final love lesson*

I'll never forget that night. All two minutes of it. Meeting a woman whom I had pegged as tiresomely mundane. A woman who couldn't possibly have anything to offer—to change me, to wow me. In truth, I wanted that cash register to be a difficult and time-consuming fix. I didn't want to leave that moment. I wanted to bask in the surprise of what this woman had given me: a simple but remarkable conversation from out of the blue. In fact, it wasn't so much what was being said that filled my spirit, but more so bearing witness to her energy.

The cash register repaired, I paid for my groceries, then turned to her. "You have a great, great evening," I said.

"And you," she said, laughing one last time. "You have an even greater one!"

*   *   *

At first she was a face in the crowd. Then she kept me guessin' until I watched her shine. And that's when everything came into focus.

Thank you, Sammy Hagar.

Ros Hill

This story is not about me. Well, it is. But it isn't...

More often than not, my name is misspelled. The vast majority of the earth's population insists on adding an additional "s" so that Ros becomes traditional Ross. Or my name is edited in the other direction and an "e" is added so male Ros becomes female Rose. It's been a hard life correcting the billions of misinformed and assuming editors.

So, for the record: Ros is short for Roscoe. (My parents shortened it just after my birth.) Therefore, if you want to add anything to my name—if that one "s" is nagging you like an evasive mosquito—then just add "coe". I have a good friend, Ross King, who tells everyone that the reason I spell my name with one "s" is because I'm illiterate. (Correction: he's not *that* good of a friend.) I tell Ross I spell my name that way in order to save ink.

Though there are not a lot of one "s" Ros' to be found, there is, however, one in particular that I would love to meet: in fact, another Ros Hill. The trick is it'll take a transatlantic flight to do so.

There is a place in northern England where I want my picture taken. All I have to do is fly to Edinburgh, Scotland, rent a car, then head south along the North Sea and make my way into the region of Northumberland. The drive will take a little under two hours. Enough time to take in the scenery and, for the first time in my life, feel as close as I ever will to the ancestral land of my distant relatives. Relatives whose names dating back to the 1700s show no resemblance to mine.

Not even close. And yet, my name—however this coincidence arose—is linked through its spelling to a place 4,700 miles away.

The place has a hill with an elevation of 1,033 feet. Its name: Ros Hill.

How strange connections can be. This odd coincidence has evoked a curiosity of unfinished business in me. I want to climb Ros Hill and look out over the surrounding countryside so that this Ros Hill can see where he came from. I want to get to know all sides of Ros Hill. I want to return with a small jar of soil from its peak. I want to ponder the possibilities that my ancestors, some 300 years ago, might have travelled there, or even stayed a night at the base of the hill, to rest for a long day's trek into southern Scotland.

We live in a time when future generations will be able to look at our lives with the click of a button. Photographs and video files will always be accessible. But no matter how advanced our technology may become, they, like us, will have to rely on written records of our ancestors who lived before cameras captured moments in time. What did our great, great, great, great grandparents look like? Brown eyes or blue eyes? Tall or short? Smiling or the hardened look from arduous labor? Endless questions that can only be answered with speculation.

But if you're lucky enough, may I suggest you go to the place where you know your oldest ancestor lived. Do whatever you must to get there—call in sick at work if needed. When you arrive, talk to the locals, talk to anybody. Listen to their accents, and listen to the way they laugh. Drink it all in. You never know what shared traits may be going on, handed down from centuries past.

Then find an open field, or a hill, and look out at the land. And there, in that moment of solitude, let your imagination open up as you watch your ancestors sitting around a campfire. Watch them sharing memories as they eat cooked meat off a stick. They are tired, and they are worn, but they are also history.

And history has everything to do with why you are who you are.

Refreshing Ice Cold
Coca-Colon

As a routine check-up, I get to have a colonoscopy every three to five years. When I go through the prep phase, I'm not only the butt of all the jokes around the house, but I'm always left feeling empty by the time I reach the hospital. What do you expect after drinking 128 oz. of sodium bicarbonate, sodium chloride and potassium chloride? I describe the solution as "distastefully disgusting" with just the hint of "nasty". It's salt water meets rancid gorilla sweat. It's what you offer someone to prove you don't want to be their friend. It's something that leaves you completely baffled that there's not one single chemist on the planet who can create a prescription laxative that won't send you into a squeamish gagging reflex. Have you seen the names the pharmaceutical companies are calling these rectal irrigation concoctions? I wonder if we colonoscopites can sue these companies for false and misleading terminology? I mean seriously…

MiraLAX (Goes down smooth like a MIRACLE!! Tastes like a MIRACLE!! It is a MIRACLE!!)

MoviPrep (It's like enjoying a great movie!! Comes in buttered-popcorn flavor!!)

GoLytely (Goes down like it was never there!! Don't take it so seriously…take it so lightly!!)

Can we please be a little more forthright by naming them what they really are…

MiraLAX (clinical name: Automotive Battery Acid)
MoviPrep (clinical name: Damn The Flood Gates!)
GoLytely (clinical name: Dear God What Have I Drank!?)

You would think the American Gastroenterological Association (AmGasAss) would be approaching the leading chemists of the world, asking them to band together and create a laxative that could leave the palate feeling savory and satisfied. We all know what happens *after* any laxative is ingested—it's sewage pipes in a state of anarchy, literally running by their own rules. But why not at least improve the prep experience? Can we please do whatever is necessary to stop the suffering? In a world of countless natural and artificial flavors, is the task to create such a wonder drink all that difficult? If so, then perhaps it's time the big players stepped in. Perhaps it's time to go corporate. Time to knock on Coca-Cola's front door.

It's an opportunity for a soft drink company to tap into the pharmaceutical market. The Coca-Cola website mentions soft drinks contain sodium and potassium. Sounds like to me these ingredients fall within the family of those found in prescription laxatives. Add some carbonation to a clear liquid formulated by a team of Coca-Cola taste experts, and you'll have created one of the most needed pharmaceutical products to date. And what will they call it? None other than:

Coca-Colon.

Of course, any new product is only as good as its national exposure. And with a product like Coca-Colon that will be revolutionizing the prep taste experience (and putting an end to every prep laxative in existence), once it hits Main Street America, there will be no slowing down its success. The key: grab immediate mass appeal with a 30-second Super Bowl commercial…

(*Music begins: "Happy" by Pharrell Williams*)

Filmed in slow motion:

A middle-age couple gleefully skip together hand-in-hand through a lakeside park, smiling like they've won the lottery. In the woman's hand is a leash guiding an equally happy cocker spaniel puppy. In the man's hand is a bottle of Coca-Colon which he's sipping through a straw. Seconds later, their hands separate and the camera follows the man skipping towards a group of runners who are congregating under a nearby 5K race start banner. As he approaches, they take notice and then divide their group in half, clearing a pathway for him to enter a Port-a-john. An obvious lapse of time shows him exiting, happily holding his Coca-Colon up high like a ceremonial Olympic torch, and then skipping back towards the woman. Embraced in each other's arms (including the puppy, playfully licking the man's face), they spin around and toss their heads back with ebullient smiles. The camera zooms in on the man who winks while taking a sip of Coca-Colon. The screen goes to red with white lettering:

Coca-Colon.
Great to the Last Flush.

Old People Day

O ld people have been around for a long time. They are masters of longevity, having outlived youth and middle age. I once shook hands with an 83-year-old custodian, whose burly grip was inescapable. He had worked a farm for the majority of his life, and his powerful hands were still seasoned with that required strength. The robust part of his life, which he carried from sun up to sun down for nearly 40 years, all began at an early age. As a kid he thrived on climbing the tallest trees, grappling large branches in order to climb to higher heights, all for nothing more than exercising his sheer durability. Old people can share a million of these moments of their childhood. And yet, as great as their accomplishments may be, when they're seen hobbling along at a snail's pace, they are still labeled as one thing: old.

Often nothing more, nothing less. Just old.

Why is youthful a word, but oldful isn't? Oldful could carry the similar type of value that youthful has. But, unfortunately, while we see young people full of exuberance, we see old people full of...old. For some reason, our thinking doesn't take us beyond their slow, shuffling, hard-of-hearing pace. So, old is a word detached from the past. It connotes a cemented state of deterioration. I'm not referring to our parents or grandparents—those whose histories we are quite familiar with, but rather the elderly out there who are complete strangers.

Old people need to be recognized. They've been youthful. They've made their contributions, and have sacrificed their time.

They've resolved countless conflicts, and have lived through times of global tragedies. They've ridden their bikes through mud puddles, made millions of snowmen, danced like there's no tomorrow, and have kissed their lovers in the rain. Everything you're doing, they've done more. In essence, they have carried the torch. They have proven themselves to being oldful.

Right now, you seniors aren't moving like you used to. You're not as tall as you used to be. Your skin has spots. Your hair is white, receding, or just plain gone. You have cataracts, crackling knees and knobby knuckles, an aching back, and countless accidental releases of trumpeting gas. You drive slowly (if you drive at all). You *are* slow. The word old sheds any past youthful attributes. You don't have a prayer escaping "old." It's almost like three scarlet letters that you must wear in public until your last days.

Yet, amongst all of this deterioration and slowness, how do we get the youth to even begin to believe that you were once younger? How do we get them to believe you once chased toads into murky ponds, or sat beneath railroad trestles, holding onto the enormous wooden support beams just to feel those exhilarating vibrations sent down from a thundering freight train? How do we let the world know that you are more than just old?

We create a national holiday, and then you guys wear a shirt. That's what we do. We call it Old People Day. If you're 75+ years old, you qualify. (You young puppies at age 74 will just have to wait a year.) We print t-shirts that have a picture of you on the front, at around age 10. Around the age when time stood still. Around the age when your youth was king. You'll wear this shirt for the world to see. Instead of impatient people standing behind you in line at the grocery store, there's a good chance they'll now be understanding and curious.

In fact, to make sure they get a glimpse into the hidden treasures of your youth, on the back of the shirt it will read:

"Tap me on the shoulder and I'll tell you a story."

Ascending

There are stretches of highway in West Texas where the road just goes and goes. Where the distance to the horizon seems as long as the horizon is wide. These are the stretches of endless miles where the mind can contemplate without barely an interruption. Where one thought can remain lodged at the forefront of your consciousness, and the only chance to escape it is to pull over and fall asleep.

For thirty minutes she found that escape in her car at a vacant roadside rest area. She reclined her seat and drifted off, entering a dream occupied by a line of ten tornados—each a different shade of blue—moving over hundreds of acres of flat farmland. Oddly, the colorful twisters were not threatening, but were, in fact, tilling the soil; working the land. And they did so in complete silence, with not a hint of tornadic turbulence. Their violent nature had seemingly been harnessed to operate without destruction. They magically swept around old farm houses and lifted safely above herds of vulnerable livestock. Families stood out in the open, mesmerized by this supernatural scene: speechless and trusting, and nearly collapsing to their knees in awe of the dutiful and attentive twisters.

When she awoke, she up-righted her seat, then rolled down her window. A comforting wind infiltrated the car, sending strands of hair dancing across her face, and triggering the memory of her dream. *The tornados…why were they quiet? Why so helpful? And why so blue?* She stared down the open road, out towards a distant mountain range. This remnant of her dream—this color curiosity, wherever it came from—felt quite real, as if it was taking shape in her conscious world. *If this wind engulfing my car had no sound, but rather color, what color might it be?* She paused, then thought, *Blue.* As soothing as one of the bluest tornados. What was the likelihood that she would have ever evoked the color blue from the absence of sound without the memory of her dream? Was this some sort of premonition? Color and sound—what was the relationship?

And that was all it took. One word—relationship—to bring back the one single thought that made her pull the car over and escape into sleep. The one thought that incessantly gnawed on every square inch of her brain: the bittersweet feeling of love.

$*$ $*$ $*$

Like so many close relationships, it was born from incredible moments, such as their first kiss in the rain. No matter how deep the thunder grumbled or how ominously the lightning struck, they were determined to stay beneath the oak tree, shielded by nothing more than a canopy of branches and leaves, and a blind faith that convinced them that their passion was unstoppable. The safe passing of the storm was a sign that no matter how chaotic the circumstances, their adrenalized infatuation would defeat all. Spontaneity was king: water balloon fights in the shower, piggy-back rides on hiking trails, making love in a clothing store's dressing room, and racing shopping carts in the grocery store parking lot. Laying side by side on a cool bed of Bermuda grass, beneath a full, burnt-orange harvest moon, nothing needed to be said. They were drinking in all the details—consuming all the things that mattered.

Yet, as much as she hated to confront the reality, one day she fully recognized that their relationship was constrained by an outside force. One that was stubbornly unforgiving, and would eventually sever their bond. As the months rolled by, and their intimacy surged well into the second year, she began to express a strong desire to have a child—the one missing link of fulfillment in her life. They would surely get married and, no doubt soon after, they would begin their own family. The topic often consumed their conversations. She was all over the map talking about the future newborn: the baby's room, stroller rides to the park, the first Christmas, the first bus ride to school, and growing old together with a son or daughter who would bring into this world a newborn as well. He didn't have much to say during her long-winded wonderings of the future. He sat silent and listened, but in his duty to do so, there was a distance in him—a separation of interest. What he knew he was certain would be the deal breaker. A thousand kisses under that oak tree in the rain bore no weight against her want for a child from her womb.

Inevitably, the investment of their passion was going to run dry. Dissolve far more quickly than it had taken to build. The future was clear: there was nothing but an imminent farewell. He held the one card that he had no choice but to play against himself: he announced that he was infertile. And there was no easy way to lower that hammer. But the news would not shake her. There was a way around this. Medical science would pull through. Certainly the brightest minds were well aware of the dejection that infertility brought. Certainly science was on the cusp of something great. But optimism sometimes has its limits. Hard as she would try to sell herself that adoption was just as viable, her maternal instincts would override it as mere irrational thinking. And as hard as she would try to be rational, one thing kept getting in the way: the essence of him. That all-encompassing feeling of love. Torn between staying with the first person who had ever offered her love beyond definition, and declining that love to seek out having a baby with another man, she found herself nowhere but lost. It was the rift in the relationship that would eventually create the final divide. The heartbreak of a star-crossed love.

*   *   *

She was done with the tears. She had wept enough in mourning of their final separation. Lord knows he was the greatest gift that she had ever received, but a child from her bloodline was the one gift that had yet to be opened. Driving on that open stretch of endless West Texas highway, she was en route to anywhere to rebuild from the bottom up. The memories of him would always be there. Outside of sleep, that was an inescapable fact. To be in love, but realizing that love wasn't enough—how would she ever be able to carry the weight of that reality? She needed a physical detachment as a whole. A fresh beginning.

For two-hundred miles she continued westward, making her way into New Mexico. The unlikely event of blowing out a front tire would lead to the first encounter of the helpful man who, two years later, would be the father of her first newborn child.

Though her husband lacked the fiery passion that poured from her previous love, she still found herself in a place of contentment. And he was, above all, a man who would do his fair share of raising a child. He was trusting and compliant. He was all that any mother or child could ask for. In times of good or bad, he wasn't going anywhere. Loyalty was a given. Nothing was more evident to prove that, than when tragedy struck.

They had taken a scuba diving trip to Belize. A 10-day vacation to do nothing more than get away and see the sights, both above and below water. It was on their third day of diving when—perhaps she was feeling a bit too confidant—she took the liberty to descend too quickly. In the process of not allowing for adequate equalization with the increasing water pressure, she critically perforated both ear drums. The result was a middle ear barotrauma—an unfavorable condition that led to her permanent loss of hearing. Unable to fly due to cabin pressure, they had to board a cruise ship in order to return home. Severe as her condition was, and recognizing there were obvious lifestyle adjustments to be made, through it all she found peace: she was his prize, and he would do anything to assist her. Though she could still speak, she felt it important to learn sign language, which they mastered in no time. In fact, they created a few original signs of their own: a fist to the head was, "coconut brain", a choke hold on one wrist was, "stop talking so much!", and a slow finger drag over the top of the tongue was, "Meet me in the bedroom". Needless to say, adjusting to the sudden loss of hearing wasn't easy. There was knowing what things sounded like, but an inability to turn up their volume from a memory. There were the days of staring at a group of trees. Just staring, and tilting her head to one side like a dog might in order to hone in a specific sound. In her case, she just wanted to hear the birds. What once had so often been background noise, was now something that she wanted to experience front and center.

And then there was the one sound that brought her down more than anything: the one sound that she had yet to hear—the first cry of her forthcoming newborn infant. An ultrasound showed that a girl was on the way. What would her voice grow to be? And if she could sing, just how would she ever capture its audible magic? Adjusting to the deaf world was work. Luckily, her husband was up for the job as well.

On a thunderstorm-infested evening, she went into short-lived early labor at their house just before midnight. Active labor was impatiently knocking on the door as her dilations were steadily increasing. This baby wanted out. It was not an easy drive for her husband as horizontal sheets of pelting rain attacked the car. They were six miles from the hospital. He had to guard his speed for fear of hydroplaning into a ditch. Beyond the beam of his headlights, everything was pitch dark. Only when lightning occurred did they get a quick glimpse of their surroundings: telephone poles, a distant barn, and trees on the horizon. The windshield wipers could not keep up with clearing the water. Just ahead he could barely make out the sight of an overpass. Despite her labor, he had no choice but to reach it and stop as the storm was now depositing golf ball-size hail. Repetitive indentions in the car's exterior were beating like a hundred drummers.

He heard them. She felt them. And then, a sudden, dense round of larger size hail pulverized the windshield, spidering cracks in multiple jagged directions. This atmospheric violence was, at last, thwarted by the protection of the overpass. Another ten seconds of fist-size hail and the windshield would have collapsed into their laps.

When he stopped the car, he signed to her asking how she was doing. She said out loud, "Scared." He held her hands, looked into her eyes, and voiced slowly for her to read his lips, "Our baby will be fine."

Seconds later, multiple bolts of lightning lit up the sky, illuminating the one thing they never saw coming: the tornado. Their car was no longer a place of refuge. He helped her out and guided her up the steep ramp that led to a rectangular concrete formation beneath the girders of the overpass. This was no easy hike for her condition. At their last sight, the tornado's location appeared to be a fair distance away, out on the horizon. But now, as they wedged themselves between the girders, they lost all view of that direction. With each contraction, she fought to make herself comfortable. The struggle to give life and to protect herself was tiresomely painful. Swirling debris began to dance in a chaotic pattern beneath the overpass. It was a calm scene, but only momentary as a straight-line gust of dirt and more debris accelerated along the highway. Part of a fence and a large section of a tree uncontrollably blew past, just missing their car. All of this she viewed in complete silence as the wind churned and carved off the top soil of New Mexico. Preparing for the worst, they forced themselves back as far as possible into their crawl space, knowing that every single inch bought them another inch of security.

*   *   *

And there she huddled, watching the scene unfold beneath her. She wondered if he could hear the twister. Was its horrifying sound on top of them? Another contraction set off an agonizing pain in her lower back—sharp as a knife, and stubbornly refusing to let up its grip. She closed her eyes tight with clinched teeth to fight it. Mother Nature might make up her own rules, but under no circumstances was she going to take away this baby.

Perhaps she was too focused on the pain of her labor, but during her battle to find comfort, she found herself sitting upright, with her back propped against a slab of concrete. Her breathing was heavy as she felt the baby crowning. Neither of them were prepared for this, but preparation was hardly a worry. For a thousand years the will to be brave had always taken on the world by itself. The motherly instinct to do whatever was necessary had always prevailed. All of her fears; all of her doubts suddenly vanished—she was going to give birth.

* * *

Beneath the dirt-covered highway overpass, he sat next to her as she held their newborn daughter—their eyes streaming with tears of undefinable bewilderment at the miracle of life. The storm, now past, left behind a trail of splintered telephone poles and trees that were stripped of their branches, entirely up-rooted, or left bowing to the earth. It also left a comforting wind that wisped strands of hair about her face. Strangely, this calming moment felt very familiar—a memory from two years past on a lone stretch of West Texas highway. It was a time of her life for escaping and starting anew. And within that remembrance there was the dream that she had always held onto: ten blue twisters tilling the soil, preparing the land for new growth. At each major turn in her life, she began to notice that there were calming moments that contained pivotal signs of promise, despite the adversities at hand. In particular, her lost first love, the scuba diving incident, and this storm had all led to something much larger than she had expected. Yes, this also included her everlasting inability to ever hear again.

Ten feet below the ocean's surface in Belize, the two of them had been looking down into the darkening abyss. This particular spot was named the Great Blue Hole, where the deepest blues eventually gave way to an enclosing darkness that plunged over 400 feet. The moment he looked away was the moment she descended, wanting to know nothing more than just how far down she could dive. But her speed was too rapid for the depths she was descending into. The pressure on her inner ears was unable to be equalized, and the uncontrolled decompression, just shy of being fatal, led to the critical rupturing of her eardrums and the ensuing permanent loss of hearing. A tragic and unforgettable moment for anyone. But for her, now holding her newborn, she recalled the undeniable allure of her ascent to the ocean's surface: the darkness that had cocooned her, had unveiled a deep hypnotic cerulean blue that, perhaps, held more beauty than she could ever handle.

That was until she looked down at the incomparable beauty of her newborn daughter who cooed softly with wide open eyes. Though this was the one sound she had yearned to hear, the moment had arrived in silence. The sound of her daughter's laugh, her songs, and her cry would forever elude her. There was no way to capture its perfect translation. It was an audible gift that only the privileged many would witness. Unless, she thought, unless...

Turning to her husband, she looked him in the eyes and asked, "Tell me...our daughter's voice...if you had to describe it in color, what color would that be?"

He smiled and signed back to her without hesitation, "Oh, that's easy....Blue."

Poor Service, Please

hat is there not to like about her? She is tall with legs that can drop your jaw like you're looking at the perfect sunset. Her thick, wavy brunette hair is cinched in a pony tail that gorgeously drapes the back of her neck. Her lips are painted crimson red. I'm not sure what she has applied to her eyes, but I'll call it "Hot Midnight Trouble". Regardless of her striking looks, my concern is whether or not she is complete with a personality to match.

Ah, here she is…approaching my table…

"Have you been here before?" she says, speaking coldly without any introduction. "Cuz if so, I can take your order now."

The toneless rush in her voice. The unfriendly, monotone delivery is all I need to know that I have just met Ms. Right. She has the perfect personality!

"This is my first time here," I say. "Anything you recommend?"

"Hamburgers. Fries. You want that?" Cold. Her voice is cold as an ice pick.

"No thank you, Jessica," I reply, reading her name tag. "I'll take a few more minutes with the menu, if you don't mind."

"Sure. Whatever." she says sharply, then leaves—obviously so disgusted with my decision to prolong my order that, if given the option, she would drag my butt back to the kitchen and dump me in the deep fryer.

Dear God, she is everything I could ask for.

*   *   *

I'll get back to Jessica in a bit, but perhaps a little clarification is needed to understand what my attraction is to this woman with a harsh personality.

She represents the exclusive group of waiters and waitresses who, I believe, were put on this planet for one purpose: to save me money. They are an elite group of individuals to whom I have no problem giving them little or no tip at all. Order a hamburger, and they'll bring you a hot dog. Ask for an iced tea refill and pray you get it before they deliver your check. The lettuce in your salad is wilted? No problem, your waiter will gladly take it back to the kitchen with the scowl of a bladder-infected opossum.

There was a time when poor service simply ate up all my patience. I'd track our waiter as he served other tables, waiting for that moment when he'd turn and I could flag him down for some extra napkins. Of course, he wouldn't turn, and I'd be left an impatient mess, tapping my fingers on the table—caught in a state of high anxiety that didn't end until I got my napkins. I became so focused on what the waiter or waitress wasn't doing that I had little time to enjoy myself.

Then, one day, a manager came by my table and asked how my meal was. "Honestly," I said. "The steak is undercooked."

"I'm sorry to hear that," he said. "Let me get you a new one."

I handed him my plate, then added, "For whatever it's worth, our waiter didn't deliver our drinks until after the appetizers."

"Really?" he said, in a concerned tone.

You would think I had just alerted him that our waiter was a Russian recipe spy. Not only was I not charged for my meal, but all of our drinks were free as well (or *comped* as they say in restaurant language). Bright light bulb goes off in my head. I start doing the math…

1 bad waiter + 1 concerned manager = FREEBIES!!

From that day forward, my perspective on quality restaurant service completely changed. What I quickly learned was that even if a concerned manager never got involved, I could at least justify tipping less because of poor service. No longer was I anxiously trying to flag down a waitress for not getting enough ranch dressing, but I was now praying for as many mistakes as possible. Don't just bring me cold soup, but take your time reheating it. Intentionally drop a couple of flies in my lemonade. I'm allergic to jalapenos. When I eat them, I break out in severe hives and itch for days. I want that jalapeno juice smothered in my mashed potatoes. If I asked for ketchup, you can bring it, but slam it down on the table like you're trying to kill a six-foot rattlesnake. And please, oh pretty please, don't smile. I want that bladder-infected opossum scowl up front and personal all meal long.

*   *   *

Now that I've clarified myself, let's get back to Jessica. She should be returning to my table soon to take my order. Little does she know, I'm going to need a couple more minutes before I decide what I want. *And just how do you plan to handle that, Jessica? Maybe just cut to the chase and spill a tray of drinks into my lap. Be my guest, sweet Jessica—I'm all for saving money by slashing your tip.*

Here she comes—woman on a mission to take my order. Hmmm….interesting…she's smiling…

"Hello. I'm so sorry I forgot to introduce myself earlier. I'm Jessica, and I'll be serving you tonight. Do you still need some more time with the menu?"

NOOOOOOOOO!!!!!!! This cannot be!! Who deprogramed my waitress!!? This is not the Jessica I knew ten minutes ago!! This Jessica is sweet, courteous, and professional. I demand an immediate explanation!!...I demand rudeness!!!

I'm searching for a reply. I don't know what to say. "I…umm…I'll take the hamburger and fries." It's the last thing I want to order, but I say it in hopes to trigger some kind of recall in Jessica's mind. In hopes she might become instantly unfriendly.

"Great choice," she says, happily. "You'll find that our burgers are quite delicious. Would you like sautéed mushrooms on yours?"

My evening is ruined. Not only will my food taste great, but I'll have to reward her for such cordial and delightful service. How could things have possibly gotten this bad? I can't take it. I'm desperate...

"No, I don't want sautéed mushrooms. But I'll take jalapenos. Lots and lots of jalapenos."

IF IT WERNT FOUR EDITORS THEN THIS SENTANCE WOOD NEVER LIKE GET CORWRECKTED.

Hug an Editor

Next to ice cold water, Velcro, a comfortable colonoscopy, and lint rollers, the one thing I am most thankful for is: an editor.

From this writer's perspective, once my stories are published, they are beautiful to look at. Commas are in place, run-on sentences are non-existent, metaphors make sense, and I look like a pro.

So, just how much disarray does an editor clean up? Or, to put it more bluntly, just how disastrous do I write?

Ladies & Gentlemen, I give to you an unedited manuscript. This one, a short horror story, might read like this…

The Day Giant Trolls Ate The Erath

Saliva like coated New York City like a blanket of contemptuous vile dog drool that was neither warm nor cold but was like *bubbily boiling like a pot of overheated rotten death. And that was like all from the mouths of 500,000,000 giant trolls!!!!!*

Once 1 troll said, "Attack and eat the Esrth!!!!!!" Then they dug theyre angry teeth into the Erath and just swalowed the dirt *like a lot. So the saliva meltted New york City just like witch vomit would!!!! No one could just run away cuz they were like so meltted!!!! And when Chicago, and London and Japan and huge other cities in the whole world got eaten it was just so totally like the worst EVER thing!!jj!!!*

67

And time was gone at the strike off the full moon in the north. Eatrh was know more. And all that was left beneeth the feet of 500,000,000 trolls was like just so much dark space that that 1 troll screemed "Now lets eat the *unaverse!!!!!*"

The End

See what I mean!?

Hey, Ref! Good Call!

If your local police department is understaffed and patrol officers job responsibilities are being stretched beyond their limits, you may have no choice but to think way outside the box for a solution, even if it means teetering on the edge of ridiculousness.

Even if it means hiring football referees.

I live in San Marcos, Texas, which is one of the fastest growing cities in the country. In addition to our population of 58,000, there are also 35,000 Texas State University students who share the same small town infrastructure. (Ever added two-thirds of a gallon of water to an already full gallon pitcher?) Throughout the day, the overflow of cars ride on each other's bumpers like a loyal buddy system. If you're first in line waiting on the light to turn green, don't get too anxious as you've got two or three cars passing through their red light with nothing going on, but their agenda. Any day of the week, you can pull up a lawn chair on the downtown courthouse square, and enjoy watching the *Running of the Reds*. Or, you can think of it as watching a movie trailer for *Fast & Furious*.

People run red lights because it's worth the risk that a cop won't be there. And in my town, the risk level is VERY LOW. There simply aren't enough officers to patrol all the traffic at downtown intersections. There's a gold mine of tickets they could be writing for running red lights, but for whatever reason their duties call them elsewhere.

Something needs to be done to put an end to this intersection mayhem that, literally, occurs throughout the day and well into the night.

I propose a creative solution...football referees.

Yeah, I know....these are the guys we hate (I'd say it's fair to use that word). However, these are also the guys we love (okay, like). As often as we are tossing verbal beer bottles at their heads, we also applaud them for what we feel are their correct calls. We are the judges of their judgments, and our likes or dislikes of their decisions are as ever-changing as Texas weather. You just never know what's coming.

I think we should deputize these guys, and make them enforcers of the law, trained to report traffic violations. Two referees will be stationed at the main busy downtown intersections. One will be equipped with:

- Official black & white referee uniform
- 1 yellow penalty flag
- 1 whistle
- 1 two-way radio
- The other referee will be equipped with:
- Official black & white referee uniform
- 1 .68 Caliber US Army Alpha Black Elite Paintball Rifle with 30mm scope, and powered by a 9 oz. CO_2 tank that includes a 200-round hopper of permanent marking neon yellow paintballs

How it works is really quite simple…

Scenario #1:
You run a red light.
Ref blows the whistle and throws a yellow flag.
You pull over.
Ref informs you that a cop is on the way.
You wait.

Scenario #2:

You run a red light.

Ref blows the whistle and throws a yellow flag.

As if auditioning for a *Cops* reality TV series, you ignore him and continue on.

The second ref sights your car in the crosshairs of his paintball rifle and, with marksmanship accuracy, tags your vehicle with a wide splatter of permanent neon yellow paint.

The police dispatcher is alerted with your vehicle description.

And here's the beauty of utilizing football referees: there are no instant replays and no opposing challenges. The ref's call is final. Still, with a head full of arrogant confidence, you blow through a red light and will soon be approaching another intersection, where, given the same opportunity, you'll do it again, as poised as a casino gambler high on his luck. Only problem is, another ref is calmly awaiting your arrival. Within his scope, he centers the nose of your car. Punch the accelerator as you may, but you don't have a prayer...the trigger has already been pulled.   At last, one thing is for certain:

You can run the red, but you cannot hide.

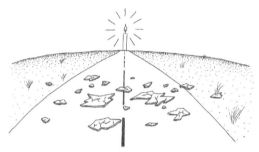

Finding Light

I drove home today, a little more cautiously than normal. Checking for the danger points: the blind hills, the children kicking a ball in the grass by the curb, the kid on the bike jamming with his headphones, and, of course, that massive semi-trailer truck, lurching out from an alleyway.

I listened to a man tell me about his highway accident. He said it's such a difficult story to tell, because he doubts anyone believes what happened to him. What he experienced. What changed him.

On a cool Texas evening, he never saw it coming...

When the 18-wheel gravel truck pulled out onto the highway, he was driving his pickup truck, approaching from behind. He knew he didn't have a chance. He instinctively blew his horn and, just as instinctively, the big rig driver hit his brakes. Smoke blew up from the searing asphalt beneath its tires. He braked hard, but the deceleration of the big rig was too sudden. Leaving little time to react, his pickup veered to the right, but could not avoid hitting the rear of the gravel truck. The front end of the pickup sheared its hood under the rig. He had one second. One second... to duck down to the right. As he fell to the floorboard, the rear of the gravel truck shattered the windshield, entered the cab, and hit his head.

Blackout. Darkness. Feeling around to touch something, but there was nothing. No left, right, top or bottom. Just a void. Complete silence. Not even the sound of breathing. But still, an awareness.

Then he saw the candlelight. A soft flicker in the distance, wavering like a dim beacon caught in a watery reflection. It grew larger, approaching him. It shifted form, and suddenly had a presence that he could not deny.

And this is the part of the story he sometimes hesitates sharing with people, because he can tell by their expressions that they doubt him. He knows they think he's making it up, but he is certain it was Jesus. "I know it sounds crazy. So many Jesus stories and so many doubters, but I'd have to be crazy to make this stuff up. And since I'm not, I know he was there. He was much larger than I could ever have imagined."

In that moment, somewhere between life and death, he says Jesus spoke and told him to open up, to no longer hold things inside himself. He had made plenty of mistakes in his life. He had stacks of regret piled high in the deepest recesses of his memory. Lord knows, he took the drinking way too far. He went on a six-year trip that led to nowhere. He missed time with his family because his thirst became a priority. He did his best to make up for that lost time. He forever ached that his spoken remorse to those he loved just wasn't enough to make things right. And then he felt it....his heart unhinged itself from all that it held. He was relinquishing himself of worry, troubles, guilt, bills, home repairs, needless knee-jerk reactions, aches and pains. He was experiencing a release of everything, because the man whom he had prayed to for so long had arrived with open arms.

In the blink of an eye, the scene changed to flickers of other lights now approaching him. Multiple colors, chaotic in a way, but arriving as a collective group. Larger and larger they grew in size and intensity, followed by a voice.

"Hey, you ok? Can you hear me?"

For a moment he felt slightly disoriented, but the foggy feeling in his head quickly dissipated, and he acknowledged with a nod.

"Look, we're gonna get you out of there. But I need you to be still. We need to cut you free. Air Flight is on its way."

Another nod, but this time with a smile. Trapped within the harsh confines of mangled steel and the shattered housing of the cab of his pickup, he said, "I'm good. Beat up, but I'm good"

A second voice could be heard. A police officer. "I gotta see this guy! He's in too good of spirits. Hey, you okay? You're in quite a mess there—my God, your head....sure you're okay?"

There was a gash in the top of his forehead, sending blood running down the side of his face, pooling on the car seat where he lay. He was able to raise his arm and press his hand against the deep cut.

Looking at his bloody palm, he smiled. He was fine. Absolutely fine. In the midst of this gruesome wreckage of leaking gasoline, disfigured doors, broken glass, and splintered steel, he had been given peace and told to move forward. He now saw a fireman approaching, carrying The Jaws of Life. He could also hear the distinct, deep thumping noise of the helicopter blades of Air Flight as it neared.

Above the pain, he smiled because he was in a place to start anew. And these people now surrounding him—what they didn't know was that, miraculously, he had already been set free.

The Bum

While I am thankful for the gift of being able to create unique humor, I am even more thankful for being able to recognize the lessons in life that humble and inspire me.

I'm not referring to how my dog stands at the kitchen door to be let out. He will just stand there and look at the door as if he were metaphysically trying to open it with super dog powers. I could use that as an example, but that isn't what I'm talking about. I mean, yes, I have learned that if I neglect opening the door, I will soon be mopping up his mess, but, still, that's hardly a life lesson. Of course, we did have a cocker spaniel named Rubbi (which was short for 'rubbish' because the garbage man had found him) who always freaked-out during thunderstorms. We quickly learned that if you didn't blockade the fireplace with chairs and sofa cushions, he would dive into the ashes and, basically, lose it. A life lesson, but, again, hardly the kind that humbled me.

To give you a better idea as to what life lessons I'm referring to, let's look at some wonderfully inspiring, narrow-minded racists in Los Angeles. I'm going to get a little help from Hollywood to make my point.

The movie *Crash* is a wonderful movie.

It's wonderful (and I know this will sound odd) because it's full of inner-city racism. From white cops who subordinate blacks, to mid-eastern shop owners who distrust Hispanics, to upper-class white women who patronize their cleaning ladies, to Asians who suspect the slightest disruption as a threat, the movie is rich with (and here's my list of wonderful words): anger, irritation, infuriation, rage, hostility, suspicion, angst, get off my property, don't touch my property, give me your property, keep out, buzz off, get a life, and, of course, I'll kill you. Everyone in the movie is a predator and everyone is the prey. It is human survival at its purest. Watch your back, or lose your back.

If all that was shown was the first half of the movie, you might come to the conclusion that it is a morbid publicity stunt aimed at persuading us to never enter the city limits of Los Angeles. If you've been there before, well, don't go back. It's looking bleak.

Luckily, the second half of the film exists, and it is that part which leads me to declare the film as wonderful. Amid the dark gray cloud of bias, destruction, and hate, there is a silver lining offered to those who have the patience and smarts to put an end to their racism. While most everyone in the movie is the problem, they are also the solution.

Though *Crash* can be seen as a study of how cultures collide with racism, as well as a study of how there is hope to end racism, I like to use the film in a broader sense, showing how people are trapped in judging other people. It is because of this judging that so many lost opportunities occur. In *Crash* there were life-altering situations that changed people and gave them new perspectives. The movie very much hit home with me, because I have been there. Not racially, but rather judgmentally. If I never paid attention to the life lessons being taught to me on the spot, then how was I ever going to change?

To illustrate this, let me take you back to my first outdoor art festival in Austin, Texas. I had just pulled up my van to my 10' x 10' booth space that was located amongst other spaces in a long row of tents to protect display walls and art from any threatening weather. As I unload my van and begin erecting my display walls, I couldn't help but notice a man who was going through some trashcans. Like any other large city, if you drive downtown in Austin you will see your share of homeless people shuffling along the sidewalks, poking their heads in trash bins and asking for money from just about anyone. Because I didn't live in the city, but in a smaller community, it was rare that I came across a homeless person. As I was there unloading the van, I couldn't help but stare and think about this grizzly, whiskered bum, whose clothes looked about as disorderly as his appearance. What happened in his past? Drugs? Alcohol? Family abuse? Why was he here? Did the festival authorities know he was down here? And for some reason, because he was missing an arm and a leg, I tried my best not to make eye contact. I simply did not want to converse (as if that would be a horrible thing). But unexpectedly, he caught a glimpse of me looking at him. In that instant, I turned my back and returned to working on my booth. I could hear the bum walking past me with the jabbing sound of his crutch hitting hard against the asphalt, seemingly making a statement in its own language. I'm sure he was en route to another trashcan, but I didn't look to see. I just knew it.

Later in the evening, the art festival opened its gates to the public. Most of the people who attended the Friday night opening were there for the wine tasting and mingling---more of a window shopping bunch. There wasn't a lot of attention being directed at serious art buying. People who walked into my booth laughed and enjoyed the art, casually sipped their wine, then went on. Nice comments, but no substantial exchange of money.

That all changed when a nicely dressed woman became overjoyed with my work. She had never seen any of my images before, and simply fell in love with them. She especially favored the painting titled, "*The Origins of Craters*", which is a scene of a herd of elephants walking away in the distance. Above them is a vast night sky filled with stars. Amongst the stars is also the Earth. Not the Moon, but Earth. This is because the elephants are walking on the lunar surface, and it is their footprints that are creating the Moon's craters. This was the original painting, and it had truly captured her attention.

"Don't sell that," she said, "Give me ten minutes to find my husband."

I had heard too many stories of artists holding art for people who said they would return to buy it, but never did, resulting in a loss of other potential buyers in the process. This being my first art show, and not knowing any better, I honored her request. Luckily for me, within ten minutes she had returned, and strangely enough in a golf cart. Seated next to her was a man neatly dressed in a tuxedo.

The man looked vaguely familiar, but I was not able to place him.

"Honey," she said to him as she got out of the cart, "Come over here and look at this. This is the painting I was telling you about. The one with the lunar elephants."

The eyes. What was it about his eyes? I had seen them before, but where? Then, the second her husband got up to exit the golf cart, it all came together. This man in a tuxedo withdrew a crutch, helping himself up and out of the cart. He was missing one arm and one leg.

The bum.

"Hello," he said, smiling with an air of enthusiasm, "My wife has told me great things about your art, and I can see she was right. This is indeed fabulous work!"

It was one of those classic Catch-22 moments: You wanted to bask in the glory of the praise you were being given, but at the same time you wanted to kick yourself for being such an idiot, knowing full well you couldn't accept the praise until you made things right with yourself. The "bum" was now standing in front of you, wearing a Tuxedo. The bum was highly articulate as he not only complimented, but applauded your work. The bum was a highly functioning human being who would soon inform you that he was not only a private donor to the local arts community, but was a volunteer who had spent all of yesterday emptying trashcans, replacing trashcan liners, and picking up debris around the fairgrounds. The bum would also, before the evening came to a close, return to my booth and purchase the original painting of "*The Origins of Craters*," because he liked to collect original art.

The bum was not only a wonderful man, but was one whose amputations I would never know the history of. In the end, that didn't matter. What mattered was the fact that he had truly humbled me. Never again would I be so quick to judge, but would always give people the benefit of the doubt.

And that is exactly why *Crash* is such a wonderful movie---full of quick, knee-jerk judgments and skepticism, but also, in the end, full of the promising possibilities of change.

Holidays

PART I
Presidents Day

I am writing this from an insane asylum. Padded walls. White coats. Horrible food. Rats in the ceiling. I had a psychiatrist friend admit me for one day and night. Just enough time to make it through… Presidents Day.

Where would we be without Presidents Day? Oh, wait! I know… we'd be at work!

We'd be slaving away on a typical, lethargic Monday, dragging ourselves throughout the office like a disoriented group of slothful slugs, greeting each other in the language of mumble, and forever regretting why we didn't call in sick.

Luckily, Presidents Day was created and our lives have been spared that one extra Monday that might've just done us in. However, there are some inaccuracies going on here that I must address. Mainly, that there are many people who do work on Presidents Day and don't have the luxury to take Monday off.

For the privileged many, most of these workers are city, state, and federal workers, as well as financial institution employees. According to the posted signs at their workplaces, will not be at work because their offices "WILL BE CLOSED IN OBSERVANCE OF PRESIDENTS DAY." They will be honoring, respecting, and observing the past Presidents of the United States.

Excuse me, while I go smack my head against the wall.

Just how do these people observe the holiday? What exactly is it that they do to pay honor to the Presidents of the United States? Do they gather their families 'round the hearth of a stone fire place ablaze with good warmth for all ye to share presidential lore of days gone by? Is this fire stoked with fresh, hearty wood cut by axe and saw in the same spirit that our forefathers must have done during the Washington, Adams, and Jefferson eras? Or are they at the public library reading volumes upon volumes of presidential history books? (Actually, they can't be doing that since the libraries are closed. So they must have checked out their books the week before.) And if they were too busy for a library visit, then certainly these people commit time on the internet, searching whatever might intrigue them, be it normal or obscure: great presidential decisions, Truman vs. Japan, Roosevelt vs. Hitler, and historic vetoes. How long does it take to mow the White House lawn? When did the White House first get central air conditioning? What President was the worst swimmer? Which President couldn't sing any better than a strangled goat? The presidential search options are endless!

But, seriously folks, are there really any local, state, federal or financial institution employees who observe the presidents on Presidents Day? I'm willing to bet one crisp Ulysses S. Grant fifty-dollar bill that not one single person exists. And if they do, they're doing it under a heavy spell of hypnosis:

Hypnotist: "Repeat after me: 'I, United States Postal worker. Do swear. That I. Skip meals to bury myself in Google searches about Rutherford B. Hayes' insistence to demolish The Great Railroad Strike of 1877'."

No, I think otherwise. I think these recipients of the presidential three-day weekend (how convenient), spend their time a little more…

Americanly, if I may coin a new word. Let's take a look at one state workers' Monday off in observance of Presidents Day. His name is Harold. He works in a cubicle in a federal building. No one, including his boss, really knows what he does. In fact, no one knows what his boss does either.

Harold wakes up at 11:35 am Monday morning. His head is pounding, severely hung over from last night's keg party at the federal building he works in. All employees were in attendance. All employees left wearing someone else's clothes. Harold, miraculously, found his way home wearing a red satin dress and cowboy boots. His Hagar slacks and Izod shirt are forever missing.

He showers, gets dressed, and eats an English muffin while watching TV. Flipping through the channels, he stares in blank engagement. Flipping, flipping, and flipping. And then bingo! He spots a channel running an ad for a local furniture store.

It's an "ALL LIQUIDATION PRESIDENTS DAY EVERYTHING MUST SELL! SELL! SELL! SALE!!!" ALL RECLINERS 50% OFF!!! ALL SECTIONAL SOFAS 60% OFF!!! AND ALL PORCELINE LAMPS 70% OFF!!!

His wife comes running into the room waving the morning newspaper in her hand. "Harold! Oh, Harold! J.C. Penny is having a Presidents Day storewide 50-75% sale on ALL BRAS!!!" She ruffles through the ad pages and comes across a full-page spread for Dick's Sporting Goods. "Oh, my God!! Dick's is having a 'BAT IT! SWAT IT! MASH IT OUT OF THE BALL PARK 80% OFF EVERYTHING SALE!!!!'."

Harold and his wife do a quick change out of their matching plaid pajamas and into some casual wear. They charge out of the house as if a meteorite had just landed in their street, and they wanted to be the first to witness its cratering impact. Into the car they jump, and off they go, headed to the beltway around town where the mega-stores are all lined up, each patriotically fronted with a ginormous American flag large enough to cover their house. Neon orange, green, and yellow signs are plastered on every square inch of store window space.

LIQUIDATION! EVERYTHING MUST GO! ONE DAY ONLY!!! Presidents Day has arrived in predictable fashion. Businesses adorned in repulsive colors guaranteeing only the best deals on the best products. Indeed, a meteorite has hit—one intent on shattering any previous Presidents Day Sale records.

Harold and his wife pull into the crowded J.C. Penny parking lot. A busy, happening place. "Look!' shouts Harold happily, "There's our post man! And there's two of my co-workers! And there's that bank teller!" Oh, what a joyous union of a privileged group. All to be found beneath the glorious sunshine in....

Observance of Presidents Day.

Excuse me, there's a knock at the door of my padded-wall room. It's two men in white coats with a straight jacket and a very, very large syringe. They could not have come at a better time.

PART II
The Blowout Solution

Let's face it, America not only excels at turning national holidays into massive blowout shopping events, but we excel at attending these extravaganzas. It's interesting how similar we treat the holidays—like it would be an abomination if they didn't scream "EVERYTHING MUST GO SALE!!!" in our faces. They are carbon copies of each other. "FOURTH OF JULY BLOWOUT SALE!!", "LABOR DAY BLOWOUT SALE!!", "MLK DAY BLOWOUT SALE!!" It's the perfect time for Discount Tire to promote a "DISCOUNT TIRE BLOWOUT REPAIR SALE!!"

Whatever happened to honoring the holidays for the reason

they were created? Yes, on Memorial Day we do recognize lives lost in the line of duty. We recognize the independence of our country with parades and large public fireworks displays. There is no denying we acknowledge holidays. But wouldn't it be nice if we let the pure essence of a holiday remain as sacred?

Why must this propensity exist whereby practically every retail outlet has to have a piece of the holiday pie? Can't we just let holidays be holidays? Do we really need our vision marred by obnoxiously massive neon yellow and green signs? Do we really need a new sofa to celebrate the Fourth of July? Why on Memorial Day do we need to get two pairs of shoes for the price of one during the "MEMORIAL DAY MIDNIGHT MADNESS & TOTAL INSANITY SALE!!"?

Before you know it, retailers are going to be cashing in on funeral opportunities.

I'll be the first I'm sure...

"We are gathered here today to not only pay tribute to the long and fruitful life of Ros Hill, but to announce the "BIG FUNERAL DAY JUST-SAY-NO-TO-DEATH BIG TENT SALE!!" going on at Home Depot all day long!! Everything is 50%-75% off, including weed killers, fertilizers, and 32-gallon trash cans!! And boy could Ros ever stuff a trash can!!..."

Oh, but the naysayers cry out to my complaints, "Holidays are major players in fueling the nation's economy." Indeed they are. Millions upon millions of dollars pass into the retailer's hands thanks to holidays. However, when consumerism overshadows the reason for the holiday, it leaves a sour taste. Like a canoe struggling in a cruise ship's wake, holidays can easily get lost in the sea of discounted sofas, washing machines, refrigerators, and barbecue grills.

Luckily, I have a solution for preserving the sanctity of the holidays.

At each quarter of the year, I propose we establish four-day-weekend holidays called, "SPEND THE MONEY HONEY

BLOWOUT SALES!!", strictly to encourage shop-'til-you-drop shopping. Let's kick-off these holidays with stores tossing out coupons and product samples to the masses lining the nation's streets in "BIG BLOWOUT SALE PARADES". The neon yellow and green poster boards will obnoxiously and appropriately decorate the floats. Massive firework-stand yellow sale signs in black wording will be pumped up and down by float-circling roller skaters, all getting the crowds amped up by chanting the holiday's anthem (imagine any kind of AC/DC song)..."SHOP OR DIE!!! SHOP OR DIE!!! SHOP OR DIE!!! SHOP OR DIE!!!..." It crescendos to such a height that some will faint from the sheer overwhelming anticipation of the four-day buying fest.

And then it'll happen: In unison, at the stroke of nine o'clock Friday morning, each town across America will fire one round from a 150mm Howitzer cannon into any unpopulated territory, such as a nearby cornfield, desert, abandoned farm house, or unoccupied IRS office.

That culminating sound of celebratory artillery—an earshot of thundering bravado guaranteed to elevate the adrenalin of any antsy shopper—shall signal the call to commence buying.

Whatever doubts may rise from fear of keeping Father's Day, Easter, New Year's Day and others sacred to their names, while not allowing big, behemoth blowout sales, will be squelched as the nation's economy will be robust and stable. People will dance in the streets wearing their new shoes and bathrobes. New owners of new and certified pre-owned cars will happily honk their horns in friendly staccato, creating nothing less than an atmosphere of utter bliss. Four times a year, every opportunity will be given for anyone to afford the purchase of a brand new Electrolux vacuum cleaner and an E-Z Boy recliner.

As for the mother of all shopping holidays—Christmas. Just what shall we do with Christmas? Shall we preserve the sanctity of that holiday?

Most likely, no. Because that one…well…that one is out of control.

Running Sdrawkcab

Every day it seems as if a latest and greatest idea is introduced to help improve your health. There are endless diets to make you want nothing more than to quit them cold turkey. There are home exercise machines that you would never allow yourself to be seen using in public (the Horse Riding Fitness Ace Power is one such piece of genius that specializes in ultimate personal embarrassment). I'm sure shadow boxing with coffee grinds in your socks is just around the corner, as is 3-meter springboard yoga diving, and cross-eyed jump roping. Of course, many of the ideas and products have a lifespan equal to that of a housefly.

I'd like to point out one idea that I find completely useless: backwards running.

The idea is that by running backwards you will strengthen your calves, quadriceps, and shins more so than by running forwards. That's all well and good, but for me the problem with the idea is that I don't run well backwards. Nor do I particularly run backwards in the safest places. In fact, there really is no good reason why I should run backwards other than for getting in touch with my inner child. (Obviously, my inner child is lacking in some departments, such as street smarts.) When I run backwards I hit things like parking signs, buildings, sturdy oak trees (they're actually worse than buildings), and old ladies (well, I haven't hit one yet, but I'm sure old ladies are much worse than trees because bowling them down requires a complete explanation to the paramedics and police as to why I was running backwards)...

Cop: "So, why did you run backwards into Mrs. Thompson? Do you realize you broke her collar bone?"

Me: "I'm so sorry, but thank God I didn't break her neck! What a mess that would've been. Look, I was merely trying to strengthen my calves, quadriceps, and shins. It was an accident. Kinda wish she were a tree, then we wouldn't be having this discussion."

Cop: "Well, we are having this discussion. And excuse me, but you wish Mrs. Thompson were a tree?"

Me: "Yeah. A big oak tree."

Cop: "Mr. Hill, I want you to stop right there with the insults. I think you owe Mrs. Thompson an immediate apology. Do you understand me?"

Me: "I already said I'm sorry. I have to say it twice?"

Cop: "You know what…I've had it with your type! Turn around, you scum. I'm cuffing you. Taking you in for disobeying a police officer and aggravated assault."

Me: "Aggravated assault!? Are you kidding me? All I was doing was running backwards, trying to put some bulk in my quads. Old lady Thompson's dang lucky I didn't knock her into a passing car. Then what would you cite me for? Murder!!!?"

(Memo to self: Do not smart-mouth cops.)

I fear an immediate sentencing of guilt is just around the corner. I fear the misinformed newspaper headlines: "ELDERLY WOMAN NARROWLY ESCAPES LOCAL MAN'S ATTEMPT TO DISFIGURE AND DISMEMBER HER WHILE BACKING UP". While "backing up" what? A car? A truck? NOOOO!!!! It was just me. It was an accident!!

So, I decide to flee the cop and begin running forwards instead of backwards. But I only get as far as the total collapse of my neuromuscular system will allow. In other words, the cop's Taser has hit, and the world goes to black.

*　　　　*　　　　*

So I wonder: Just how important is strengthening my calves, quadriceps, and shins, if I'm going to have a high chance of ending up in jail or suffer other dreadful outcomes? If I run backwards along a lake trail, it's a given I'm going to trip and take a dip and, in the process, hit my head on a large rock. If I run backwards in Ireland, I'm going to be the butt of the jokes at the pubs. If I do it in New York City…well, forget it—I'm not attempting to run backwards in New York City. Really, the only place that I can run backwards safely is the Bonneville Salt Flats in Utah. Oh, how convenient.

Of course, proponents are out there. According to runaddicts. net, there are many benefits with running backwards:

It will improve your posture.

Wrong. A few hundred falls on my tailbone and one trip into the lake, I will have no posture.

Your senses will be heightened. Your peripheral vision will become more acute.

Are you kidding me? I need eyes in the back of my head. Literally!

You will have fun.

Pay me about ten grand and I'll have fun. Last I checked, I never found running into revolving doors, mail boxes, construction workers, city buses, cactus, my mother-in-law, or man holes as necessarily being fun.

You can still run while you are injured.

The last thing I want to do is something completely counterproductive while healing an injury. Look, after just five minutes of running backwards, rest assured I won't be running backwards. I'll either be in the Emergency Room, the Operating Room, or the morgue.

Maybe I got it all backwards about running backwards. Maybe I simply need to accept that I am a backwards failure, and should move forward with my life. It's a wise suggestion, but there is a problem: I am a very curious person, and now fear I might try an alternative to normal forward running.

I am a slow learner. Watch out people, because here I come… running sideways!

Austin's Finest

I have a rubber bracelet I wear around my right wrist. Half of it is faded black while the other half is of a pale flesh color. Six years ago it was midnight black and fire truck red. The band no longer has anything written on it as time and sun have faded all the words as well. But the bracelet is there to stay for as long as it will remain intact. After all, it's always nice to hang on to a little memento to remind me that not all hardcore softball coaches are always what they appear on the field.

When I was coaching select summer softball, there weren't many teams that looked forward to playing Austin's Finest. They were a very talented and competitive girls softball organization based out of southeast Austin, Texas. All the girls were Hispanic, and were born and bred with a voracious want to win. They were skilled, quick, scrappy, and they were strong. They had very high softball IQ's, which meant that they saw and understood all the subtle nuances of the game. They knew a batter's hitting direction based on that batter's stance and history. They could judge the speed of two runners on first and second, and given a live ball, they could make a split-second decision about which base to throw to in order to ensure an out or a double play. And in those situations there were always players backing up the bases in case of an overthrow (which was rare given their innate throwing accuracy). When they were on base, they were incredibly deft at stealing bases. They were all of this and more at the ages of 11-13.

They were coached by Jose Hernandez who played to win and always demanded championship production out of his girls. He was not only a crafty coach who knew every strategy in the book, but he ran a very tight ship that wasn't too happy with sloppy play. He was what many of us would describe as textbook hardcore. Make a mistake or two out on the field and you didn't hear about it when you came into the dugout, but rather you got an ear full right then and there.

I too coached to win and was very competitive. I favored constructive criticism with an encouraging tone. If you observed Jose and me coaching against each other—analyzing our coaching styles— you might very well conclude that, win or lose, I was the softer one; perhaps offering a more supportive environment than what the players on Austin's Finest were experiencing. Or so I blindly thought.

If you *really* knew Jose, you'd soon discover his heart pounded proudly and compassionately for every single player on the team. He wasn't so much hardcore as he was simply preparing them for high school softball and, for many, the collegiate fields where the world is very unforgiving of errors (especially repetitive errors). And so Jose would scout the tournaments and pay close attention to whom he figured he could develop to play at the next level. He forged a team around a philosophy of work ethic that demanded nothing less than 100% focus. He was smart, savvy, confident, and intimidating.

Still, his coaching style rubbed me the wrong way. I figured he was on a mission to suck the air out of the fun balloon, completely deflating it. One day, after watching Austin's Finest lose a game to a fierce competitive team, I intentionally stood near his post-game huddle with the players. I wanted to hear just how out of control he could get. I wanted to witness him unleash on his team. I stood there waiting for hurricane Jose to hit, but pretty much heard nothing more than a man sincerely addressing his tired team with an understanding heart of gold. Every single girl had her eyes locked on his as he panned their faces, firmly pointing out the faults of the game, but at the same time sympathizing with the present burden of defeat. And then I saw it…the smile. The smile as warm as a campfire. He would remind the girls that it's just a game. He knew that life has so much more in store for them than just softball. Sometimes you get to pick your battles, while other times the battles are dealt to you. Either way, Jose knew his players needed to understand to always give it their best shot. That's all he ever asked of them. He then extended his arm. "Hands in," he said. Twelve girls extended their dirt-coated, sun-burned arms, resting them upon his. This was no tyrant, but, unbeknownst to me, a true leader whose criticism was constructive and spoken with an admirable, encouraging tone.

This was Jose Hernandez. This was the same man whom I would later see that summer standing by his dugout, talking to a teenager whose hair and eyebrows were non-existent. A boy who had that appearance of having gone through some sort of medical treatment. A boy who was, in fact, 15-year-old Joshua Hernandez. He was undergoing radiation and chemotherapy for the removal of an advanced stage of a brain tumor called a medulloblastoma. I had heard about Joshua from my son, as they were in the same class. But I had no idea of this connection, that Jose was his father.

In the fall of that year, I was attending a high school football game and saw Jose handing out red and black colored rubber bracelets that were embossed with: "Josh Hernandez. Faith is my strength." Josh was smart, strong, and extraordinarily humble. He never wanted the spotlight; he just wanted the love and the laughs. After a hard fought battle, Josh passed away at the age of 22. Never once did those defining elements of his priceless character ever cease to exist.

It's only natural that Josh was an incredible person—after all he was cut from the same cloth of the man I had once pegged to be insensitive. I was fooling no one but myself.

To you—Jose and Josh, I hold my glass up high with a hand that bears a six-year-old, faded black and red bracelet. Literally, not a single day passes when I don't touch the bracelet and feel its smooth worn texture. It's not as colorful as it used to be, but that's superficial and a meaningless fact. What matters is that it reminds me daily of how great a person Joshua Hernandez was. Like sunshine raining down from a giant blue sky, Josh soaked up all the love that fell his way. And it spilled right over into his father's lap who knew more than anyone that life is so much more than just a game.

A First Taste Of Metal

It took her nearly 95 years to hear it. When she finally did, you could see the look in her eyes as she sat in the car, staring hypnotically at nothing in particular as her vision seemed to fall just short of the dashboard.

I had come to train Rouye Rush on a Saturday morning at The Wellington—her senior apartment complex that had a small, but adequate fitness center. As I pulled into the main parking lot, I saw Rouye standing under a tall shade tree. I had been listening to music in the car when the thought occurred to share a couple of songs with her.

I rolled down my window and pointed to the passenger's seat. "Why don't you get out of the heat and have a seat. I want you to hear something."

For six years I've been training Rouye, who's hardly your typical almost-centenarian. There is a durableness about her physiology. Though her skin is thinning, it is the musculature beneath that refuses to weaken. A year ago she was sidelined from working out due to an outbreak of the shingles virus, leaving her legs aching and itching for weeks on end. But when she did return to the gym, it was as if she had never skipped a beat. Pushing 130 pounds on the leg press wasn't much of a challenge. Perhaps the secret lies within her motivation. Ask her to throw a 20-pound medicine ball five times against a wall, and she'll give you ten. Ask her to dribble a basketball in a figure eight pattern around her legs and, for the first time in nine decades, she'll get it right by the third try without any sign of hesitation. While she knows her limits, and easily recognizes when something is beyond her abilities, Rouye has an open mind that welcomes trying something new. Even if it's, well…a bit shocking.

Enter: Heavy metal music.

Sitting in the passenger's seat next to me, I turned to her and said, "Rouye, before we hit the weights, I want to play some music for you."

"Okay," she said, "Let's hear it."

I had my iPod hooked up to my car's auxiliary outlet.

"How many songs do you have on that thing?" she asked.

"Over two-thousand."

"Good lord," she said shaking her head. "When does anyone find the time to listen to two-thousand songs?"

"I know it's a lot," I said chuckling at her surprise. "But I love my music."

"Well, that's pretty obvious. Okay, so what do you want me to listen to?"

"Metal. Heavy metal."

"Metal? Of course it's heavy."

"Metal, Rouye, is a type of music. Like rock, but harder. It has an edge to it. It's not uncommon for the singing to be full of rage."

How could I have *not* lost Rouye? I might have been better off describing Michelangelo's Sistine Chapel painting in pig Latin.

Classic get-to-the-point Rouye stepped up. "You're not making a lick of sense. Just play the song."

"Okay, okay…but there's a reason I want you to hear metal."

"Which is?"

"To show you just how talented these guys are—just how gifted their voices are. Trust me, you're not going to like this first song. But bear with me, and let me surprise you with something."

And that's when I cued up my iPod to the song *Down With The Sickness* by the group Disturbed. All it took was the song's opening tribal drum beat making way to David Draiman's corrosive and guttural voice, to elicit a lifted eyebrow of uncertainty from Rouye. Approaching 95 years old, and I had invited her into my car to get a shattering head full of heavy metal. Could her morning start any worse? What nightmares might she potentially have had as she settled into sleep that evening? Gargoyles hovering above her, playing 12-string bass guitars? Or her freefalling into the molten caverns of inner-earth, while weighted down in a suit of medieval armor?

I made sure to cut those possibilities off at the pass, by playing just enough of *Sickness* to give her a taste of heavy metal music. There was no way I was going to inflict the entire song upon her. "What do you think?" I asked.

"What do I think? What's he saying? Why's he barking like a dog?"

I couldn't help but laugh. "A dog... ha! But, I know...I hear ya."

"And this is what you wanted to share with me?"

"Actually, yes. But there's more to it. You know...don't ever judge a book by its cover." I scrolled through my playlist of Disturbed songs until I found their version of Simon and Garfunkel's *The Sound Of Silence*. "This is what I want you to hear. It's David Draiman—the same guy you just heard sing. But this is his other side that not only illustrates his passion, but just how gifted he is."

All it took were the first nine seconds of a piano leading to Draiman's tender and beautiful voice. So rich and captivating, you have no choice but to stop what you're doing and listen. And if you're Rouye Rush, you have no choice but to experience a reverent silence of admiration that slips you into a hypnotic trance just short of the dashboard.

Hello, darkness, my old friend
I've come to talk with you again
Because a vision softly creeping
Left its seeds while I was sleeping

It's hard to find a song that evokes as much emotion as this version. I'll never forget the sight of Rouye Rush. Four months away from 95 years of age, and caught in the soaring notes of a heavy metal singer. At first impression, she's not quite sure if the distorted style of his voice is, in fact, singing. But make way for her open mind, and moments later she can't believe that *The Sound Of Silence* is performed by the same person.

"He needs to do more songs like that one," she said. "It's beautiful. Really beautiful. That song was meant to be sung that way."

And that's where I turned off the music, and we left the car to go work out in the gym. As we walked, I couldn't help but look at her and think about how different she was compared to the ten thousand people mentioned in the song...

> *And in the naked light I saw*
> *Ten thousand people, maybe more*
> *People talking without speaking*
> *People hearing without listening*

David Draiman's voice had delivered the song's message like no one had done before. And Rouye had not only heard it, she had truly listened.

Because

As children, we grow up using the word "because" as that single most ineffective way to explain ourselves by relying on one word that explains nothing:

Mother: "Why did you trip Allison at school?"
Daughter: "Because."
Mother: "Because why?"
Daughter: "Because."

"Because" becomes rooted as one of the most go-to words in our vocabulary. And even as full-fledged adults it's not unusual to regress to our childhood and resort to the single word reply, which typically is amplified in a moment of heated impatience, and often preceded with the word "just."

Daughter: "Give me one good reason why you won't give Justin a second chance?"
Mother: "Because."
Daughter: "Because why?"
Mother: "Just because!"

From out of the rubble of their disagreement, the word "because" prevails and stomps its heavy foot in the face of the daughter, leaving behind an unfinished dialogue that has nowhere to go but six feet under. Realizing the conversation is dead, the 19-year-old daughter gathers her belongings and heads out the door to her car. She backs down the driveway in arrant disbelief that her mom could be so adamantly against Justin. As she pulls away, she sees her standing behind the screen door, with arms akimbo, a face of stone, and penetrating eyes that, all combined, sheer away any possibility of Mother, and leave an unbending matriarch.

*   *   *

From the beginning, their conversation went nowhere but down....

Daughter: "Headed out to a movie. Back later."
Mother: "You and the girls?"
For a moment the daughter hesitates, then gambles on the slim chance that her mother might actually not be objectionable.
Daughter: "Actually no. Justin's back in town"
Mother: "You can't be serious."
Justin. The leader of the pack. Always in cahoots with those she deemed the undesirables. Their compasses pointed to mischievous true north.
Mother: "You know that boy is a dead end."
Daughter: "Mother, please don't start this again. Justin's not what you think he is."
Mother: "Oh, you're so right. Forgive me for forgetting how he nearly killed you driving his car into that brick wall. Forgive me for missing that minor detail."
Daughter: "That's not fair, mom. He swerved to avoid hitting the boy on the bike. He saved that boy's life. And, no, he didn't nearly kill me."
Mother: "A boy who only you saw. The police report showed no one but you mentioned him. No boy was ever interviewed. Even he didn't mention a boy. And you know why, don't you?"
The daughter stood silent. Her mother was right. She had been the

only one who saw the boy. She broke his hands free from the steering wheel and pulled downward, steering the car hard to the right, saving the boy's life, and, in the process, sending the car into a blunt impact with the street's curb. The car's forward momentum surged onward before coming to a complete stop into the unyielding brick wall of a corner drug store.

He was drunk. He told the police he never saw a boy. He could've said he did, and gone with her story. It would've at least given him a dash of heroism, softening the critical and irate blows to follow. Though inebriated, he was coherent enough to do what was right: to stick with the truth.

Daughter: "That was a year ago, Mother. He's changed. He's not that guy anymore."

Mother: "Look at his father. He's no different. You can't deny influences."

Daughter: "And you, Mom—a person unwilling to give second chances—am I to be influenced by you?"

The strain of even thinking of Justin, burrowed beneath her skin like a relentless parasite. Long before he turned 20, she had seen his mischievous ways. The kid in grade school who thrived on instigation. She had pegged him early, and, once pegged, she was never one to forgive. Second chances didn't have a prayer. Nonetheless, her daughter had raised a valid point. One that she didn't want to agree with, but one that reverberated pronounced sense. But this conversation, this repeat of mother-daughter tension didn't take long to make one sick of arguing. Sick of even having to consider her daughter's point.

Mother: "Listen to me! Do not go out with him!"

Daughter: "Give me one good reason why you won't give Justin a second chance?"

The matriarch knew it was best to be short and emphatic.

Mother: "Because."

Daughter: "Because why?"

Mother: "Just because!!"

And at that moment, your 19-year-old daughter leaves. Separated by a screen door, you watch her with your heated eyes. Down the street her car vanishes around a corner. Long before you can even close the door, you are nothing but an afterthought. She knows Justin's story like no one else. She knows the sound of him crying frightened in the tight clutch of her consoling arms. She knows the misery he lives with daily, thinking about what if he had hit that boy on the bike? How could he possibly outlive such a tragedy? A life encased in regret.

How painful can a second chance be? How painful can it be to trust your daughter's choice? Sometimes the most liberating moments can be setting someone else free, and the reasons for doing so are numerous.

And why should you do it?

Because.

Let The World Know

My senior year of high school in Illinois, I was ranked #2 in the state in the long jump. I remember showing up at track meets and hearing the whispers around me: "That's the guy." Being aware of that notoriety fueled my adrenalin and sent me soaring outwards near the 23-foot mark. I loved to jump. I mean I really loved to jump. I was dunking the basketball three years earlier as a sophomore. By my senior year I had an entire repertoire of dunks. I was demonstrating raw talent. Today, 38 years later, I put in the training and dunked it at age 55.

And that, my friends, is called bragging. The boastful stuff that swells your head like a pumpkin on steroids. As if that wasn't enough…

My best 5k time is 16:08. At age 50 I ran a 4:45 mile. I've held my breath underwater for over 3 minutes. My lowest recorded heart rate is 38 beats per minute.

Massive pumpkin. Hard to fit into an elevator.

Six years ago, on a Carnival cruise ship, I won the ship's free-throw shooting contest. I went three rounds deep in the playoffs, before sending a 19-year-old baller from New York back to his stateroom, crying like a pathetic mama's boy. (Okay, so it was only me that saw it that way. Big deal.) I was awarded the exclusive, highly decorated golden plastic trophy. Last year, on a Royal Caribbean ship, I was bequeathed a golden First Place medal for winning the Western Caribbean Golf Tournament. (Okay, so it wasn't really a golf tournament. So it was a 9-hole, super tiny, miniature golf course, sandwiched between the sport court and boogie board surfing simulator. Big deal.) But I sank a hole-in-one to go into sudden death with two other players. Two holes later, I was crowned Champion. Amidst my playing up the ridiculousness of attaining such "victories," there was a part of me that wanted it publicly known what I had accomplished. And so I did it via non-verbal bragging. I wore that silly medal to dinner that night. Wore it like I had won an Oscar. *That gold medal around your neck—what did you win?* "*Oh, I never thought you'd ask! Well, let me tell you…*" And while I suck at real golf, that night in bed, I replayed the hole-in-one as if I'd just discovered something as unbelievable as unfolding the secrets to time travel.

We are born, and then we die. And in between what did you do? What was it that set you apart from the ordinary?

I say, brag about it. Don't be so modest that on that final day of your life, as you lie immobile in a bed, you have a head full of incredible, but unspoken laurels. Don't pass from this Earth, leaving it up to a family member or a collage of photographs resting on an easel to finally give insight as to what you accomplished or what you dearly loved. Let those laurels be the ones that you can truly rest upon. Don't wait a lifetime to finally divulge.

You're telling me she wrote all of these poems? They are so profound. Who would've thought she could write like this? I would've loved to have talked to her, to learn from her. I had no idea!

He was a water skier? He built that magnificent tree house? Seriously, all of those are his medals from the war? I had no idea!

Ever notice when an older person shares (or even boasts) of all the places he has travelled to, or speaks of his many achievements, that we listen without complaint, without ridicule of him being too prideful. He's 91 years old and, instinctively, we feel obligated to give him our attention. His life is wrapping up. Let's find out who he was, what he did, how many grandkids he had, what kind of car engines he liked to tinker with, how fast he ran. If he never took the opportunity to brag about himself, then, for sure, give him free range to do so now. The clock may be ticking, but it's never too late.

Bragging is defined as the act of talking boastfully. To be boastful is to show excessive pride and self-satisfaction in one's achievements, possessions, or abilities. What I'm encouraging people to do is to pull back the harness on the arrogance that is associated with bragging, and to convey something in a more tame boastful manner. Simply put: speak proudly. *Soft brag.* Unlock the magical unknowns that truly define who you are, and let them run loose in the streets. Don't put a leash on them. Let them forever run free.

I have a strong curiosity about people. Not so much about what they're doing, but rather what they've done. What is the history that has made them who they are? What obstacles have they had to overcome? What surprising humanitarian deeds have they done? What has defined them that they can brag about? Perhaps you weren't much of an athlete, or never had the time and money to travel, and so achievements such as those never fell your way. Maybe you looked obesity square in the eye and said, "To Hell with you!" and proceeded to drop the pounds, promising yourself every day to never give up. 70 pounds later, as you stepped onto the scale, you nearly dropped to the floor sobbing with joy. Perhaps you have experienced other things that also penetrate our emotions: rescuing a suffering animal, surviving a near-fatal car accident, or beating cancer.

And then there are the moments we take for granted that could use a good bragging. The diamonds locked in our memories. Taking your 4-year-old daughter to the river and letting her see her first family of snapping turtles, where not a word was spoken, but just the look in her eyes, large as Chinese lanterns. Those big baby blues consuming the sight of six turtles soaking up the sun as they sat motionless on a log rising out from the water's rippling surface. So you were never the fastest runner, the highest jumper, or the strongest swimmer. So you didn't have athletic ability. You lead a very simple life, and never cracked open a talent that set you apart from the common folk. Then, as you and your daughter strolled the banks of the river, you found yourself with an enthralled curiosity about all the interdependencies of plants and wildlife. Understanding wildlife habitats, aquatic ecosystems, and the hierarchy of the animal kingdom came easy, as you learned not from books, but rather from immersed observation. In a relatively short amount of time, you would later start a nature tour company, all because you had the gift of opening people's eyes to the subtle nuances of nature that could so easily be overlooked. This journey of discovering yourself, of finally grasping what sets you apart from others...perhaps it's time to brag. And what better reason to brag if your daughter was the main catalyst.

Don't hold it in. Set aside modesty and advertise yourself for just a bit. You don't have to do it in such an arrogant fashion that your legacy will teeter on the brink of disaster. Simply speak up a little— nice and proud. Just enough to let the world know you were king for a day.

Coffee

When I tell people that I've never tasted coffee, you'd think I had announced that I've never seen a bird before, or tied my shoes, or even heard of the game of baseball. They look at me completely befuddled. *And what planet are you from? Have you seen a psychiatrist for this? It's never too late to seek help.*

Once during a formal dinner at a high-end restaurant in Chicago, a waiter approached my table of ten and asked if I'd like an after-dinner roast. I looked at him and said, "No thank you. The one I had for dinner was just fine."

He said, "A coffee roast."

I looked around the table at nine befuddled faces. *Did I say something wrong?* Little did I know, I was burying myself under a dog pile of ignorance. "Beef." I continued, "It was roast beef. Remember? You served it to me about twenty minutes ago."

Wiping off the look of (you guessed it) exasperated befuddlement, the waiter smiled at the other patrons, from whom he received normal-people answers. It took me a bit, but, in the end, I figured out their sneaky coded language about this roast beverage. And while I wanted to feel no more of the oddball than I'd already become, I feared if I did order an after-dinner roast, I'd spew my first taste across the table like a high-powered fire hydrant. I chose the safe route and said, "Some more water, please. Thank you."

You think I don't blend in well amongst coffee drinkers in restaurants, then you should see me in Starbucks.

I'm a Starbucks manager's worst nightmare. While everyone and their dog is ordering coffees, lattes, espressos, and racking up the bill, I'm this guy...

Starbucks Manager: "Welcome to Starbucks! How may I help you?"

Already, I can't speak. I'm drowning in a sea of alien coffee terminology as I stare at the overhead menu. *Caffe Misto. Iced Coffee. Cold Brew Coffee. Skinny Mocha. Cinnamon Dolce Latte. Caramel Macchiato.* I'm thinking since when did coffee get to be so complex? It's got to be a chore to decide what you want. But, then again, I don't even drink the stuff, so what do I know?

I know one thing: this guy sure could use an answer.

Me: "You have so much to choose from."

SM: "We most certainly do! Starbucks prides itself with a large variety of tasty options. Would you be interested with an espresso?"

I honestly don't even know what an espresso is. I'm guessing it's a term Fed-Ex has coined for overnight shipments to Mexico... *"Send your package ESPRESSO!!"*

Me: "Does an espresso taste like coffee?"

SM: "It's thicker than coffee, brewed through a pressurized process that involves very hot water and finely ground coffee beans. Has a wonderful creamy consistency. Would you like to try one?"

Me: "Well, I'll be honest, I've never tasted coffee before. I'm not sure I'd like it."

There it was—that look of befuddlement.

SM: "You've...never...tasted...coffee...before?"

Me: "No. Never. Just as I've never kissed the belly of a pig."

SM: "But you've kissed other parts of a pig?"

Me: "No, I didn't mean to imply that."

SM: "Well, you did, and to that I say, to each his own."

Me: "Look, I don't kiss pigs, period. All I'm saying is that I've never tasted coffee before."

SM: "I gathered that. But as a little bit of advice: the pig analogy makes you seem….well, rather odd."

Me: "I'm not odd!"

SM: "You say that, but you've never tasted coffee."

Me: "And that makes me odd?"

SM: "Very."

I looked around the cafe at the tables occupied by customers sipping their morning brews. Bent over and engaged in little whispers, aghast at what they had just overheard.

"Did you hear that? Did you hear about the pig man?"

"The who?"

"The pig kisser…that guy at the counter. He doesn't drink coffee. Rather odd, huh?"

"Hell yes that's odd. Are they his pigs?"

"Oh, I'm sure they're his pigs. Probably babies them. Makes them oatmeal for breakfast."

"Coffee with that breakfast?"

"Maybe for the pigs, but not him. He's just too odd."

And that's where it all comes back to—the fact that I am on oddity. I don't drink coffee, therefore I might as well be put on exhibit next to the bearded lady or the man with three belly buttons. I absolutely love the smell of freshly brewed coffee. I love to stick my nose inside a can of coffee grounds, and inhale it like it held the secret longevity to life. If it led to pure bliss, I could snort a line of grounds off the kitchen countertop in order to kick start my day. The smell of coffee has it all. But to taste it—I have no curiosity. Oddly.

So, why is that I don't drink coffee? What's the story behind my dysfunction? I think it has to do with my preconceived notion that people who drink coffee appear more adult than those who don't. There is something about a person holding a steamy cup of coffee that immediately settles them into a state of registered maturity. They speak with slow and proper annunciation—their word selection being delivered with confidence and ease. They are calm and reserved.

I, on the other hand, exit Starbucks with only bottled water in my grasp. As I walk down a rain-soaked sidewalk, I come to a large puddle and contemplate what my chances are of clearing it in one long, leap of faith.

My chances are slim, but honestly the kid in me could care less.

It's Time to Tranquilize
Hotel Managers

Twelve hours on the road, and all you can think about is a hotel room. Drop your suitcase, and flop onto the bed like an uninhibited free fall into a swimming pool. Twenty minutes ago you exited the highway, anxious to free your vision of a hundred thousand segments of broken white lane lines. You don't need anything fancy—just a bed to plunge into sleep. The La Quinta Inn will do just fine. You park the car, then walk inside to be greeted by Carol— a middle-aged receptionist at the front desk.

Carol: "Hello. Welcome to La Quinta. How may I help you?"

You: "I just need one room for myself only."

Carol: "King or queen size bed?"

You: "Queen will be fine. All I need to do is crash."

Carol: "That'll be four fifty five. Check out is 11:00AM. All I need is your license and a credit card."

You're standing there ever so slightly wondering if maybe, just maybe, you misunderstood her. There's a slight snicker in your voice.

You: "Uh, how much for the room?"

Carol: "Four-fifty-five."

Yep, you heard her correctly.

You: "Like four-hundred and fifty-five?"

Carol: "Yes, sir. Formula One is in town."

You: "But I'm not here for Formula One. I'm just a tired guy who's been driving for twelve hours and needs a bed to crash on."

Carol: "Sir, I'm not quite sure if you realize who you're dealing with. This is not just La Quinta Inn. This is the hotel industry. This is the one worldwide entity that can jack prices so high, you have no choice but to hand over that little plastic card in your wallet and pretty much consider yourself screwed. And you can kick and scream and go into demonic gyrations that'll look like you need an exorcism, but the bottom line is: we ain't budging. Now, will that be credit card or cash?"

I understand the supply and demand going on here, but is it really necessary for hotels to hike up room rates as exorbitantly as they do? When Formula One was in Austin, Texas, the Best Western in a town 30 miles away charged $450.00 for a regular room. Whatever happened to hotel managers treating customers like customers and keeping prices steady, regardless of what's going on in town? Did the hotel industry ban them from working? Were they fired for dishonorable greed? Were they scooped up by a front-end loader before being pureed in a gigantic blender, and then poured into the Hudson River? I say we do some undercover work by collecting the names of all hotel managers who are participate in these 400% rate increases, and treat them as they should be treated.

I got a plan…

We'll start by hiring an expert marksmen to wait outside their residences. With a tranquilizer gun they'll shoot the managers in the rear as they bend over to get the evening paper. (Aiming for the rear eliminates the risk of hitting any major organs. Plus, when you see someone with a feathery dart lodged in the buttocks, there's a sort of comical *Three Stooges* added bonus.) If they don't subscribe to the paper, then they'll be shot as they head out for an evening jog. If they don't jog, then our man on the streets will hit them in the grocery store. And if they only eat delivery pizza, then we'll pay the delivery driver to put them in a headlock and rotate them so their rear faces the street...bulls-eye! After being tranquilized, we'll microchip their hands which will be nonchalantly scanned at any point-of-purchase to verify identification. Typically, the scan will read: "GREEDY SOB", "BLOOD SUCKING VAMPIRE", or "NOT A NICE PERSON". Once identified, "Operation Screw You Hotel Manager" will go into full effect...

Convenience Store Cashier: "One Snicker bar. Will that be all, sir?"
Hotel Manager: "Yes."
Convenience Store Cashier: "That'll be $15.99."
Hotel Manager: "Excuse me—did you say fifteen-dollars and ninety-nine cents!?"
Convenience Store Cashier: "Yes, sir. Formula One is in town."

Yard Sale Homeowner: "You'd like to buy the measuring cups set, Monopoly game, and flat-head shovel?"
Hotel Manager: "Yes."
Yard Sale Homeowner: "$320.00"
Hotel Manager: "Outrageous!! Formula One!?"
Yard Sale Homeowner: "You got it, buddy."

Honda Sales Rep: "So you'd like to buy the used 4-door Accord with 57,000 miles?"
Hotel Manager: "Yes."
Honda Sales Rep: "That'll be $520,999."
Hotel Manager: "I know, I know...Formula One."
Honda Sales Rep: "Actually no, that ended yesterday. But this is the Day After Half-Price Sale. Now, how would like to pay, sir?"

It's time to give hotel managers a taste of their own greed by letting them know what it's like to live on the other side of the counter. After all, these guys are making movie theater concessions prices seem as if the popcorn is just being given away.

Classified Ad: *In the market for a new job? Seeking a career change in a field that thrives on taking advantage of its customers? Then perhaps a hotel manager is your calling—no previous job experience needed. Only the mental skill set of a bank robber.*

It's a cultural phenomenon how we accept increased pricing set by hotels due to holidays, seasons, and local events. Even though there is as much a demand for food, fuel, and toothpaste as there is a place to sleep, we don't see grocery stores price-shafting us because there's a college graduation going on: *"College graduates and families—Welcome to Gas-N-Go Mart! Fuel your car here for only $17.00 a gallon!! Then grab a freshly-cooked rotisserie chicken, bag of chips, and a soft drink for just $99.00!! And what better way to end the day than by cleaning your teeth from a $15.00 tube of toothpaste!!"*

Yes, these are certainly exciting times when the economy is so robust you can throw customer service out the window, and simply implement a mad price hike to get all you can get. When Formula One is in town, even churches should charge people to put money in the offering plate, or at least establish a $20.00 minimum. Look, guys, do you or do you not want that new Sunday school wing built before Christmas? Follow the hotel industry's lead and, before you know it, your monetary needs might never require another single prayer again.

Hallelujah!!

The Rabbit

The moment I jabbed my foot hard to the right was the moment I felt my right knee buckle. I collapsed down on the court, watching the hot-handed 18-year-old kid I was defending rise high above me, rhythmically settling into perfect shooting form as he swished a game-ending 25 foot three-pointer. The perfect shot that I was doing everything in my power to disrupt, deny, and dismantle. My infamous, confident last words to my teammates moments before the shot was taken: "I got this guy!"

This was a noon time pick-up game at our local Activity Center. There was no game clock, no fans, and no refs. Just ten guys out to work up a sweat, and each one of us detesting the taste of losing. Down I went to the hardwood, and once I made my way off the court, a substitute player was hollered in from the hallway to make me history. That's how we roll. The game must go on.

And off I went, hobbling out into the parking lot with what I was certain was a strained knee. Within an hour it swelled like a prized water balloon. Within two hours I could barely bend it, as if concrete had been injected. Within three hours I pretty much surmised that this was something more than just a strained knee. Within four hours I was wondering if how I was feeling could be diagnosed as acute, irreversible, clinical depression. Luckily for me, I put my knee through a battery of self-diagnosis tests: a little jump here, a little side step there, and some hands-on massage to gauge joint stabilization. My findings: I had dodged the bullet. I had not torn my ACL.

* * *

"You tore your ACL," said Dr. Ivy, after contorting my leg at various uncomfortable angles. "This joint is pretty loose. Of course there's the off chance that it's a partial tear. The MRI will tell all."

Dr. Ivy is a highly respected orthopedic surgeon in our town. It was only natural that I tried to push her initial diagnosis a different direction. "But is it possible that it's just a really bad strain?"

"I doubt it. I think it's torn. But yes it's possible."

Later that day I had my MRI. I saw Dr. Ivy the following morning.

"You didn't tear your ACL."

Just as I was about to do a one-legged jump off the table and ecstatically jump into Dr. Ivy's arms, she added, "You shredded it. It's totally obliterated."

Due to my scheduled out-of-state travel plans, the surgery was performed a month later. Two days after the operation, I asked Dr. Ivy about my most pressing concern: "When can I start jogging?" That's all I cared about. I've been a runner and basketball player since I was ten years old. I competed in the state track meet in five events my junior and senior years in high school. When I was 50, I ran a 4:45 mile. At age 53 I could still dunk a basketball. Many of the greatest moments of my life have pivoted around my knees. And then, I made the decision to show the world how to stop a punk, hot-handed teenage three-point sharpshooter.

"You can start light jogging around four months as long as you do exactly as you're instructed." Dr. Ivy looked me straight into the eyes, "Do not overdo it. Listen to your body."

I listened to my body and progressed exactly as planned. I was slow jogging at four months. I was picking up speed at six months. Nine months post-op, I was performing introductory lateral movements. At a year I was at full linear speed. Everything was back to normal except for one small detail: I was unsure of myself being able to move laterally on the basketball court. Or, to be more specific: I was unsure of my knee.

As that one year mark arrived, I recalled Dr. Ivy telling me about a one-legged hop test. She said it was a test that actually entailed measuring more than just the distance you could hop on one leg from a static position. It also measured hesitancy, which indicated how confident you were about landing on the involved leg. The test was administered to patients who were released to full activity. "Your reconstructed ACL is strong and stable," she said, "The question is how stable is your confidence? How hesitant are you about landing on the healed leg? You'd be surprised how many people just stand there, not wanting to perform the exercise for fear of blowing the knee out again. At some point, you have to completely trust yourself."

The day Dr. Ivy released me to full activity, I put on my workout clothes and stood on one leg on my back deck. For the longest time, I stood as motionless as a flamingo. Then I hopped for what I think was the distance of maybe three inches. I had the confidence of a mouse entering a rattlesnake den. I firmly planted both feet onto the deck, turned around, and went into the house to eat ice cream. What was it going to take to trust that my knee wouldn't collapse beneath me?

*   *   *

About a week after I chickened-out performing the one-legged flamingo test, I let our rat terrier, Domino, outside to take care of his morning business. It was a cool, foggy morning with plenty of dew blanketing the lawn. Typically, Domino will take about five strides in the yard, hike up the leg, and then immediately make his way back to the house. On this particular morning, Domino stayed out longer. I had not yet put in my contact lenses, but I noticed movement as I looked through the kitchen door window. (Without my contacts my distance vision is a blur. Stand out there in the yard 20 meters from me, and ask me how many fingers you are holding up. I can practically guarantee I'll say you aren't holding up any but, instead, what appears to be a pitcher of lemonade or something just as incorrectly obscure.) My nebulous farsightedness detected a small black and white blur speeding along the backyard fence line. The blur then made an abrupt change of direction and went back from where it came. Then it reversed its direction again. I squinted my eyes to sharpen my view and noticed that Domino was chasing a rabbit. I quickly opened the door and, in only my underwear, sprinted barefoot out into the wet yard. The only sounds were that of his rapid footsteps and collar tags jingling. There was no barking or growling, for in the heat of the chase his internal hunting mechanism was locked in for the kill. And my Save-the-Rabbit mechanism (otherwise known as a soft heart) was locked in on Domino. Keeping low to the ground and as agile as possible, my feet jabbed to the left and then, a few strides later, back to the right, quickly pushing off after planting firmly into the dewy turf. Frightened by my pursuit, the rabbit relentlessly darted back and forth, staying close to the fence in hopes of finding an escape route. It was doing everything in its power to out maneuver us, but Domino was gaining, and within seconds had his mouth clamped around the rabbit's tail. And that's when I bolted from a low angle, laying myself out into the air, tackling Domino. I kept him in my grasp, as the two of us slid across the wet grass and careened into the fence. I knew he wasn't happy with me. I had spoiled the hunt by being a rescuer instead of a spectator. During the short time frame of the tackle, the rabbit broke free from Domino's jaws and found an exit point at the bottom of the fence. With grass stains from shins to chest, I laid in my underwear with my dog panting heavily in my arms while his lips smacked bunny fur. And amongst that wet, dirty mess, a revelation hit me: I had taken my reconstructed knee out onto the proving grounds and pushed myself beyond hesitancy. As the sun hit the horizon, it quickly dawned on me how many sharp lateral moves I had just performed on slippery wet grass. This was more than a one-legged hop. This was everything Dr. Ivy had told me I needed. I stood up and realized how stable my knee was. It was raw instinct in my quest to save the rabbit, and in the process I had discovered confidence.

I went back into the house and gave Domino a dog biscuit as a consolation prize for not getting his rabbit. I swear there was a moment of disgust and reluctance as he beamed his eyes at me and slowly opened his mouth to accept it. I cleaned myself up before putting on my socks, running shoes, workout shorts and, of course, my contact lenses. Walking back out to the deck, I positioned myself only on the leg with the repaired ACL. And then, in a moment of no second thoughts, I flexed my knee and single-leg jumped up and out, airborne for the longest and happiest one second of my life.

Six Times Was All It Took

There is nothing more impressive than watching a grown man on a mission, as he walks over to a chair and kicks it. Kicks it as if it had actually done something horribly wrong and needed to be punished immediately. As if that chair had a mind of its own, manipulating cunning schemes designed to mess with your mind until the end of time. After all, it would only seem logical, rational, and fair to presume that because you just cut your thumb open with a knife while trying to carve the furry skin off a kiwi fruit, that the chair sitting over there in the corner (yes, the one intentionally hiding from you) is the real culprit for your now bloody problem. No second thoughts are needed. Just drop the knife, make a beeline to the chair, and kick the living splinters out of it. There, that'll make things right!

I met a college student the other day at a local gym whose right hand was wrapped with an ungodly amount of that all-too-common, unstylish, flesh-colored, ACE elastic bandage wrap. So heavily wrapped, it was as if there was a football concealed inside. You could also say he resembled a fiddler crab with that one lone enormous claw (in this case, a mitten). He was walking around the gym trying to figure out if he could lift weights without enduring too much pain. After watching him finish a set of agonizing, grimace-on-the-face barbell curls, I became curious about his injury.

"So, what happened to you?"

"Oh, just a little accident."

A "little" accident? Been juggling chainsaws blindfolded lately? "Looks like you really did a number on it. Break anything?"

He lowered the barbell to the floor, accompanied by the grimace that simply didn't want to go away. Raising his massive mitten, he exclaimed, "Yes, I broke three bones."

"And may I ask, what was your little accident?"

"It was a door made of steel. I punched it a few times."

Looking at his bandaged hand, I couldn't help but wonder: *Just how many times was a few? Are we talking thirty punches? Forty?*

Hardly. He told me he hit the door six times. Six times he attempted to knock that door off its hinges and send it flying into tomorrow. Six times was all it took to realize he didn't have a seventh punch left in him. The bones were screaming for him to stop. He looked down at his mummified hand and spoke with profound wisdom, "Steel doors don't budge."

No kidding, Sherlock. And all it took was six George Foreman's to figure that one out.

"My girlfriend just really made me angry. It was a stupid thing that set me off. Just stupid. Don't want to talk about it." Of course, it's always a girl.

Well, good thing the steel door took the blame, because otherwise there might not be much left of her. I didn't pry into the details of his personal affairs, but I can only imagine how the conversation probably went...

Her: Honey, I hate to break the news, but my parents are going to
    stay with us for a month over Christmas.
Him: BOTH of them?
Her: Yes, and their four dogs and the goat.
Him: Wait a sec. BOTH your parents and a *goat*?
Her: And four dogs.
Him: I got that, but a goat?
Her: They thought it was a stray puppy on the highway. Pulled over

and put it in the car. By the time they got home, the goat was riding on dad's lap with its head out the window, tongue lapping in the wind. So, he's a keeper. They named him Buckle Up.

Him: Four hyper-yippy Pekingese dogs, your parents who are notorious for clipping their fingernails at the dinner table, and now a goat named Buckle Up? A *month* of this? *WHERE'S THE STEEL DOOR!!!!!!?*

Whatever it was that he couldn't talk through with his girlfriend, he should've at least punched a bag of cotton balls, pulverizing each and every one down to their very last tiny fibers. Even a box of cereal would've sufficed. But he saw that 250-pound rectangular punching bag, and just had to pick a losing fight. In the heat of his anger, he tossed the Give-It-24-Hours rule to the wind. Instead, he opted for the least rational route and, in the process, racked up a not-so-pleasant medical expense of having to cover his $3,000 health insurance deductible.

Your girlfriend said something you didn't agree with. It hit a nerve. It happens. But you shot off like lightning towards that steel door. This thing we do as humans, having to unleash our destructive energy on inanimate objects—aren't there better options? Here are some suggestions (they'll save you major medical expenses, as well as having to replace things you once purchased to enhance the beauty of your home):

- Go for an all-out sprint around the neighborhood, even if you're in your pajamas, *GO!* The neighbors will understand.... *"Oh, look Harriet! It's the neighbor running like a crazy man. But bless his heart. Sure beats throwing the computer off the roof!"*
- Take your temper tantrum out to the backyard and try jumping rope with a 25-foot water hose.
- Bike to the next town.
- Hyperventilate until you faint and shut up.

- Stick your head in the garbage can and scream like a rock star.
- Try to hold ice cubes under your armpits for 10 minutes. When they're all melted, the rage to deal with them will have completely neutralized all that venom coursing through your veins.

If those suggestions for calming your psychotic behavior are beyond your grasp, then I've got one more to offer (which, in fact, is probably the best advice):

Take your hot-headed disposition face-to-face with that steel door and, right before you strike the first blow, try unclenching your fist, turn the doorknob, and put one foot in front of the other until you find yourself outdoors in the therapeutic open air. Once there, take a deep, calming breath. I bet if you have any sense at all, you'll soon discover a path of least resistance…

Go *talk* to your girlfriend.

Twig

Lauren was 20 years old when she woke up on a bed of hay in the landscaping trailer. She was the rear passenger on a motorcycle that had collided with the pickup truck towing it. You would think that when you're catapulted from traveling at a high rate of speed, your flight would be nearly as fast, and your trajectory would lead to no happy ending.

For Lauren that was not the case. She recalls it was as if something had gently guided her into that trailer. As if something were looking after her. To this day though, she has no idea what that something was.

But what she does know is that had it not been for the trailer being in the right place at the right time, chances are she would not be here today. Nor would she have had the chance many years later to read the name tag of a 91-year-old grocery store employee. After all, it was the name tag that made all the difference.

Strange coincidences are always the best. Even if they take nineteen years to occur.

*   *   *

It all began in 1997, in a high school English class taught by her mother, when the name caught Lauren's attention: Terwilliger. Such a different name. But a fun name. A name whose syllables playfully skip off the tongue. It could be a character from a book of fables... *Prince Terwilliger raised his golden sword atop his winged stallion.* It could be a hobbit....*Terwilliger was the greatest carpenter of all Middle-earth.* Or it could even be a gift shop...*All bracelets are 50% off at Terwilliger's!*

It could also be the name of a professional baseball player.

Wayne Terwilliger is his name. He played in the major leagues from 1949-1960. He was a second baseman, drafted first by the Chicago Cubs before going on to play for four other teams. His most notable experience was with the Brooklyn Dodgers when he played alongside the great Jackie Robinson.

From the moment Lauren came across his name, it became a part of her life—infiltrating her in such a way that she felt committed to it. She used it for computer pass codes. She said Terwilliger was worthy of being the name of her first-born. Though said in jest, the statement had a sincere undertone—a way of acknowledging that no other word rivaled it. What was the highlight of her English class? Reading a short essay by Annie Dillard entitled "Terwilliger Bunts One". Just saying that title made her smile. An audible alignment of words that sounded perfect. As if better off with no spaces: Terwilligerbuntsone. It became a catch-phrase that she would never forget.

*   *   *

Nineteen years have passed since her high school English class. Lauren has spent time broadening her horizons by travelling to Korea to stay with a friend and explore a culture literally foreign to her. She visited Hawaii to learn about the healing powers of herbal medicine. But it is her love of music that guides her to an occupation suiting her perfectly. She acquires a degree in music therapy that channels her passion to improve the lives of people with autism. The non-threatening medium of music reaches far into their psyches where other methods of treatment have not. The music taps into the tight crevices of the brain that struggle to make sense of things most people take for granted. It's a masterful style of therapy that opens up the mind, instead of confusing it.

Lauren's life has been well-travelled and not wasted amongst the bane of typical everyday living. She's favored taking the paths that explore her curiosities. It has been a productive life that has also encountered the miraculous....

* * *

It is summer 2016, and Lauren is driving on I-20 with her 2-week-old daughter, Dorothy, to a pediatrician appointment in Ft. Worth, Texas. Halfway into the thirty-minute trip from her home in Weatherford, Lauren realizes she is out of baby formula. The small town of Aledo is just ahead, so she exits the highway for a Brookshire Brothers grocery store. Grab the formula off the shelf, put a few other items in the basket, pay the cashier, and off you go. What could possibly interrupt such a simple errand? Perhaps a name tag.

What happened next came with no warnings. No signs indicated something magical was about to occur. There was no strange feeling like the time she went airborne from the motorcycle and felt as if some kind of guardian had steered her safely into that bed of hay. There was nothing like that. There was only a 91-year-old man watching her struggle with her bag of purchases while trying to maneuver Dorothy back into her car seat. He was an employee of the store who often helped customers with their groceries. He offered his help, which she accepted, and when he finished she noticed his name tag.

"'Twig'," she said. "Now that's an interesting name."

"Oh, that," he said, smiling. "That's actually my nickname."

"It's a great nickname," she replied. "It's unusual. In fact, I have an unusual one myself. For the longest time, people have called me 'Linky'."

"Well, Linky, my real name is Terwilliger."

Lauren did a double-take, uncertain if she'd actually heard him correctly. "Did you say...Terwilliger?"

"Yes I did."

"This is so strange, because I've always loved that name. Came across it in an English class. There was a baseball player named Terwilliger."

Caught in a moment of disbelief, he paused, reciprocating the double take, then said, "That's me. I'm Wayne 'Twig' Terwilliger."

Two people. Neither knows the other, but they are immediately connected through the magic of a wonderful coincidence. It is a moment rich with immeasurable value.

When you're 91 years old, you can pretty much say that you've seen and heard it all. You've got more memories than there is time left on the earth to tell of them. But each day that you awaken leaves an opening for something new, and perhaps something unlikely. The marvel of an improbability will always be welcome. After all, having the soul stirred with amazement simply never gets old.

Lauren told him of the essay she had read that introduced her to "Terwilliger" and went on to explain how much she liked his name. The coincidence of her crossing paths with him was something they both found unbelievable. Unable to wait till he got home to tell his wife the news, he called her from the store.

It took nineteen years for Lauren to finally find a person whom she had never been looking for. For nineteen years she had never forgotten about the allure of Terwilliger. But what were the chances of meeting him without any premeditated plan? Her nickname, Linky—was there any possibility that it was in some way a clue or premonition of things to be *linked* by some unexplainable cause? And was it at all possible that whatever had guided her into that soft bed of hay had somehow been involved, directing Lauren's path to Aledo, Texas? It's anyone's guess.

At the time that Wayne Terwilliger called his wife, Lauren took out her cell phone and dialed her mother. "Mom," she said. "Remember my English class you taught back in 1997? Well, have I got a story for you…"

&#@%!

The Ending I Never Got.

Three years ago I had a pleasant encounter with a friendly motorcyclist. At a busy intersection on the campus of Texas State University, I gave him the right-of-way. He raised a thumbs-up while giving me a thank-you nod. I followed him in the rainy, congested morning rush hour traffic, making sure to keep a safe distance between us. Such cordial driving. Such respect for each other. Such a wonderful morning.

Such an outright lie.

*   *   *

Three years ago I had a rotten encounter with a jerk (okay, he was a motorcyclist). I didn't give him the right-of-way, because I couldn't— he was driving by his own rules. He appeared unexpectedly, having taken the bicycle lane to avoid waiting in line like everyone else. As I took my turn to proceed into the intersection, he ran the stop sign and, without looking, cut directly in front of me.

The instant had arrived—that immeasurable fragment of time when a mood can turn a one-eighty with no warning whatsoever. Your mind is sailing under blue skies on an ocean calm. How is it possible that not a single tremor was felt before the tsunami unleashed itself right before your very eyes?

This is wrong. This is very wrong. And I'm supposed to abide by the laws of your free will? I'm supposed to just sit back and accept your crass and conceited misconduct? My hand hovered over the horn. If I don't honk at him, he'll go about his autonomous way, feeling almighty and exclusively untouchable. If I do honk at him, I risk the chance he might want to defend his own wrongful actions no matter the repercussions. But *wrongful* hits me hard, and I can't stop myself from wanting to call him out. This, however, is not my common territory. I'm a patient and forgiving guy. I've never been in a fight. I don't prefer agitated situations. But in this instant, he exudes an attitude that I just can't let continue. I will always give someone the benefit of the doubt, but I doubt this guy can benefit from anything except for someone to confront him.

I lay into my horn with a heavy hand that doesn't give up for a good five seconds. I give a momentary pause before I hit it again. As I'm hoping the sound waves will shatter his helmet, this is the precise moment when the tsunami hits. He takes both hands off the handle bars, raises them in the air, and proceeds to emphatically flip me off with a double-bird.

How quickly I wanted to floor the accelerator and stamp him into the pavement. He blatantly runs a stop sign, disrespecting everyone, then expletively defends his actions. Sure, I pushed him to that point, but still, all that he is doing is wrong.

There were no more bike lanes for him to cheat the system. We were in a single-file line of stop-and-go traffic comprised of college students. Judging by his backpack, he was probably one as well.

My daughter—who I was taking to class—was sitting next to me. As my eyes were intently burning through the windshield, I'm sure she was wondering if this moment were marking the beginning of irreversible insanity. *Ladies & Gentlemen, This is my dad about to lose his mind. He's not happy with the motorcyclist. Whatever craziness happens next, I'll be sure to pass this on to my grandchildren—a story for the ages..."Grandchildren, gather 'round and I shall tell you the story of my father, about the time his mind went bat-shit rabid..."*

Here's the part of the story that truly spotlights one of the more colorful and intellectual conversations I've ever had. (Okay, so maybe not quite a conversation, but more like an exchange.) My horn wasn't doing a good enough job as my spokesman, so I rolled my window down, craned my neck out and, completely oblivious to the incoming rain, yelled, "Are you serious!!?....ARE YOU &#@%!ing SERIOUS!!?"

My fervid state of agitation had become embalmed in a hoard of analogies. My mouth had become the proverbial raging bull. My temper was tornadic. I was a heat-seeking missile, or perhaps more accurately put: a fully loaded F-16 Fighter equipped with nothing more than a load of hostile F-bombs. Like an emergency siren, my voice had no restraint with its harsh emissions. My entire &#@%!!ing projection was aimed at annihilating the &#@%!ing enemy. My concern of self-dignity was as non-existent as a beggar heckling for money on a crowded city sidewalk. And amongst the sea of students walking to class, they were the least of my concerns as my bombs rained down upon these civilians as well.

I can't stand being part of a public scene--being that person who becomes the target for anyone's ridicule. That person who becomes known as *"that person"*. And there I was…that person. But my consensus was: *Oh, well, guess I'd better finish what I started.*

I told my daughter to roll down her window. "But it's raining," she said.

I gave her the look: *ROLL…DOWN…THE…WINDOW*. There was no hesitation. She rolled it down.

The motorcyclist had moved his position to the far right, as he was sizing up the narrow gap between the line of cars and the curb. I moved my car over to the left to ride the broken lane line, and then inched forward so that he was in full earshot near the front right corner of my car.

"Hey, you &#@%!ing idiot!! YOU'RE A COMPLETE &#@%! I SAID….GET THE &#@%! OFF THE &#@%!ING ROAD!!!!"

Such maturity. Such an exemplary father. Such an angry rut I was stuck in.

The line of traffic we were in led to an intersection at the base of a hill. This is where the motorcyclist and I would go our different directions. Of course, I had to have the final say.

For some reason (and still to this day I don't know why), when it was his turn to pass through the intersection, he crossed the street then positioned his motorcycle sideways, so to have a better view of me. Perhaps he wanted to follow me, to get my license plate numbers, or just give me a good ol' stare-down. I proceeded through the intersection, my pathway taking me right by him. I ever so slowly crept past, and in the heat of my boil, pointed my finger at him and said not a word, but simply let the weight of my gesture speak for itself. His helmet had been on this entire time. He gave no response. For all I could tell, he was frozen.

* * *

I hadn't driven two blocks when I realized how I would've done anything to turn back time and erase my trail of anger. How certain I was of myself for letting this guy know that his self-imposed rules of the road do in fact have repercussions. People like myself will aggressively ride his tail. But all that I had done was so unlike me. I had been in the same situation countless times, and had always let things slide.

Just before I dropped my daughter off for class, I said to her, "You know, all that stuff I said back there, all that rage…I can't believe I just did that. And now that it's all done—this feeling stinks."

"It's okay," she said, "He shouldn't have run that stop sign like he did."

"Yes," I replied, "but I shouldn't have acted how I did. It was stupid."

I was overcome with regret. I wanted to drive back there and offer to buy him a coffee or breakfast, or something where we could sit and talk it out. Discover some kind of common ground where we could both acknowledge our faults. And if, in the process of that offer, he might chose to flip me off again, then so be it. But at least I would've felt good for having tried.

The reality is that I never did drive back to find him. I let that opportunity slip away and, instead, chose the path of least resistance by going onward about my day.

I've been kicking myself ever since.

I Pledge Allegiance
to the Trucks...

Ever notice how many times your patience won't even extend itself beyond the windshield of your car? It's early evening, and you're cruising along the three-lane highway, enjoying the uninterrupted flow in the left lane. You're headed home from work, 10 miles to go. Monday Night Football will be on in 60 minutes. You've already called in a pizza to pick up on the way in. There is no rush. What could possibly set you off?

And then it happens—something that you've instinctively predicted: 70,000 pounds of a freight-haulin' semi-trailer has just moved over into your lane to pass a car. 70,000 pounds that is not exactly turning over the kind of speed you're trying to will it to possess. How quickly it becomes not your day. Basically, in your mind, you're screwed. You're losing precious seconds in a race that's not even a race. Your flow has been interrupted, and that is enough to wish you had a missile launcher bolted to the top of your car. *Does this guy have any idea how much he's inconveniencing me? What is his deal!? Just gimme one shot!*

For two miles you remain behind the big rig. Two of the most aggravating miles you've ever endured. How is it possible that such tragedy has been borne into your life? As if some higher power has been tracking you, and then, in an unexpected decision of spontaneity, roars in great exaltation: *"THAT MAN THERE! THE ONE BEHIND THE TRUCK...HE SHALL SUFFER A PAIN LIKE*

NO OTHER!!!" And suffer you do. 120 seconds of hemorrhaging impatience, bleeding profusely from the center of your brain. Finally, as the truck moves back to the center lane, you accelerate past him, shaking your head in frustrated disbelief. In your mind, the truck driver has not only disrespected the unimpeded flow of the left lane, but has also proven that he is nothing more than 18 wheels of utter inconvenience. Your last emphatic, grumbling thought as you exit the highway: *Trucks!!*

Trucks.

They transport 70% of the country's freight. Where would we be without them? As you make your way to pick up the pizza before settling into Monday Night Football, you will have the luxury to do so because of trucks. The car you're driving wouldn't exist had trucks not delivered the separate parts that combine to make the car. The pizza will be freshly baked, boxed, and ready for pickup when you arrive because trucks delivered the framing lumber, sheet rock, nails, screws, plumbing and all else down to the napkin dispensers that make Perfect Pizza as perfect a pizza palace as possible.

The comforts of our homes exist all because of trucks: sofas, beds, sinks, air conditioning, spatulas, toilet paper, and that magnificent, rectangular household staple that radiantly illuminates Monday Night Football into our living rooms.

Trucks keep us well fed. They keep us clothed. They build us airports, skyscrapers, water parks, and zoos. So involved are they, that they help us heal the sick and mend the wounded. And while life is being restored on one floor of a hospital, on another, trucks are playing an integral part of providing supplies that help bring new life into the world.

Yet, as much of the world that they move in order to make the world go round, what is it about our impatience with trucks? Why are we so annoyed when a semi moves into our lane of traffic, causing only a relative blip on the radar delay in our travel time? Why is it when we want to park at a grocery store, but have to wait as a truck maneuvers itself into the unloading dock to deliver all that we buy, that we are looking for the first sign of an opening to swerve around it? For all that they do, seems to me that we should be getting out of our vehicles and dropping to our knees to pay homage to these miracles of transport. Anyway we can include trucks into our National Anthem? The Pledge of Allegiance?

"I pledge allegiance to the trucks of the United States of America..."

Forget the Super Bowl. Let's have Beyoncé and the Red Hot Chili Peppers shakin' and jammin' on top of a semi-trailer parked on the 50-yard line at the NFL's Championship Freightliner Bowl. Move over Benjamin Franklin... we're inking a big rig right smack dab on the face of the one-hundred-dollar bill. And why not honor trucks with the Transcontinental Red Carpet Highway—an exclusive coast-to-coast (literally) red carpeted freight interstate system where never an impatient car driver shall ever roam.

Regarding the issue of our impatience for trucks...what's it going to take for it to sink in that trucks are the backbone of making things possible? Perhaps we should pass a law requiring mandatory ride-alongs in big rigs. See the world from a truck driver's perspective. See what it takes to back up a 53-foot tractor-trailer into a narrow unloading dock. See that when a truck changes lanes on the highway, it's not an attempt to annoy you, but to simply get around the car slowing them down. Are you enjoying your dinner at Red Lobster? Ever wonder how that food got to the restaurant? Good lord, give the truck a break. Until we finally come to understand, admire, and honor freight trucks, our ignorant impatience will forever continue to be an embarrassment to ourselves.

Remember: 70% of the freight in this country is delivered by trucks. Strip that down to 20-30% and you'll have your dream highway of zipping along with so few big rigs to worry about. Of course, it'll come at a cost as hospitals will lack surgical equipment, tire shops will lack tires, grocery stores will lack produce, and construction sites will have so much idle time that the workers will do very little but play washers in the dirt. And those who won't be playing washers will be at home, laid off from their job. And you could be next.

As much as you may not like to hear it, that lumbering 18-wheeler whose rear wheels are riding the curb in an awkward right turn in order to deliver a mega-load of products to Home Depot, is one of many such vehicles you depend on.

Perhaps the time has come to exercise patience. Perhaps it's time to ease up on that accelerator, and embrace a world where drivers cordially wave trucks into their lane of traffic.

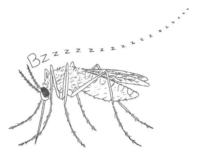

Culiseta

If you were to have seen me, I must have looked like I had lost my mind. It was nighttime, and a full moon's soft glow illuminated my dashboard. I was alone in the car, in the parking lot, slapping myself in the face. Not just once or twice, but numerous times—as if my hands were being controlled by some mad puppeteer. My ears took most of the hits. Sharp, stinging slaps that accomplished nothing.

And just what was it that I was trying to accomplish, you might ask?

Murder. Cold-blooded murder. Even if it meant my suffering some facial lacerations, I was intent on delivering death to a mosquito.

The trick was locating it. You'd think killing a mosquito shouldn't be much of a chore. I am, after all, about a million times larger. I have a daily regimen of going to the gym to lift weights. Compared to the mosquito, I possess the indestructible cross-bred strength of King Kong, Hercules, and Chuck Norris. I can rip off the wings from a mosquito's thorax in the quarter-blink of an eye. I can blow the bug off my arm with relative hurricane force. I can annihilate it in any manner I desire just as long as I can…locate it.

And this is the part where all of my robust power falters like the graceless floating ability of a cinder block. This is also the part where I am convinced that the incessant buzzing next to my ear is, in fact, the sound of a mosquito's joyous laughter. With each failed slap to the face in the parking lot, my car rocks like a baby's cradle. Yes, I put that much effort into it. It is literally slapstick comedy that is literally bugging me. Its buzzing laughter appears to be hovering no more than one inch from my ear. Slowly, I raise my flattened hand to a spot about a foot out from where I detect the sound. The hovering laughter has not stopped or moved. How can I possibly miss? I take one deep calming breath before I commence with the slaughter.

W H A C K ! . . . W H A C K ! ! . . W H A C K ! ! ! . . . WHACKWHACKWHACKWHACK!!!!!!!...

There is now silence. The car stops rocking. I look at my palm to find no signs of murder. Seriously!? Then I hear it: bzzzzzzzzhahahahah!!

WHACKWHACKWHACKWHACKWHACK!!!!! Repeatedly, I continue to strike out at the plate. This is infuriatingly frustrating. How is this even possible!? Miraculously, my hand and upper jaw bone are not broken. And though my ear hasn't fallen off the side of my head, it is, however, throbbing as if swollen to the size of a football.

By mere coincidence, I have a book on the passenger's seat titled, *Insects*. A friend had loaned it to me to read about a certain caterpillar that is infesting my oak trees. Curious, I look up the mosquito to get a better look at whom I am waging war. Turns out it's a woman. Or so its name appears.

Culiseta longiareolata.

Culiseta. Sounds so feminine. I'm impressed that scientists gave the mosquito such a beautiful name. Still, what did I ever do to anger this flying woman?

Culiseta my love,
Oh how you hover above,
And buzz so close to my ear.
Please depart from this place,
Or I shall smash your face,
And never again call you my dear.

Her laughter stops. My car fills with silence. Perhaps during the whackfest I might have maimed her, shattering a couple of her legs or rendered her blind. Culiseta did all she could do to maintain flight, but, in the end, pain and exhaustion got the best of her. Perhaps she plummeted to the floor behind my seat, where she shall spend her final hours entangled in dirty carpet fibers.

And then, I feel it—my ankle. That all too familiar itch immediately following an insect bite. Except mosquitos don't bite, but rather pierce your skin with their head syringes and suck your blood. I react quickly and scratch my ankle like I'm certain it's a winning lottery ticket. Of course, the more you scratch, the worse it gets. As my lottery ticket fails me—and out of pure irritation—I do what I always do: I rake that ankle deep and raw until it goes numb. In 24 hours I will have a scab a half-inch wide by two inches long. All from a spot that began no larger than one-tenth the width of hair follicle.

I'm now fit to be tied, caged, locked-up…euthanized. I don't care who hears my raging voice: "CULISETA!!...WHERE…ARE... YOU!!!??"

Another skin prick hits the other ankle. A third one lands on the upper calf. And a fourth one needles me behind the knee. No buzzing. No laughter. She is the ancestry result of over 100 million years of mastering stealth assaults, and she is on a mission. Hell hath no fury like a female mosquito in attack mode.

I open up the *Insects* book next to me. I'm curious about her anatomy, specifically her head syringe. It's called a proboscis. Turns out Culiseta is quite the drinker, as she can consume up to three times her body weight in blood. I read on, until I am interrupted by her buzzing. Only this time it's not by my ears. Culiseta, for whatever reason, is bouncing around between my dashboard and the windshield. She is not only completely exposed, but has set herself up for total inhalation.

Four times with the back of my hand I try to smash her against the windshield, jarring my knuckles hard against the glass. She makes her way to the tight crevasse where the windshield meets the dashboard.

All I can do is dart my fingertips into that confined area, gnashing more of my knuckles as I try. I look for a towel, a pencil, anything to assist in the jabbing. I have no such item, until I remember that I keep a pocket knife in my glove compartment. Rummaging through miscellaneous stuff and numerous oil change receipts, I find the knife buried beneath the clutter. Pulling out the blade, I scan the dashboard and see that Culiseta is quietly positioned in the crevasse. This is my chance.

It will be a difficult jab as I'll have to hold the knife from the end of the handle with my thumb and index finger in order the wedge into her confined location. Cautiously, so not to disturb and send Culiseta into flight mode, I position the tip of the blade two inches from her…

*   *   *

100 million years of ancestry. Culiseta's lifespan is but a microcosm of that as she should perish within 42-52 days from her birth. Like any insect, there is nothing to be learned. They do as they are genetically instructed to perform. Wasps and bees simply *know* how to build their hives. There was no schooling involved. Mosquitoes know how to extract blood and reproduce more mosquitoes. They know how to transmit diseases. They know how to annoy. From the perspective of certain animals, mosquitoes are known to be a source of food. Culiseta is part of a complex food web within the animal kingdom. Perhaps this is destined to be her lucky day. I cannot deny the cunning fight she put up earlier. I cannot deny her ability to evade punishing blows to her fragile existence.

The grip on my pocket knife loosens. I pull the blade back, having come to the conclusion that, as bizarre as it is, I am going to free Culiseta into the night air. This compassion towards an insect that has nailed me four times in the leg, and has made me slap myself at least twenty times in the head, just doesn't make sense. But, then again, maybe it's not supposed to. Maybe I'm simply going on my genetic instincts.

Rolling down my window, I manage to shoe her off the dashboard and out of the car. I actually smile at this act of kindness. Life, I say to myself, is good.

Did I Lock My Car?

People, there are not enough criminals to go around. And if there were, they would not be rising at the crack of dawn to steal your stuff, including your car.

But there you are, living in small-town America, on your way to the grocery store to get a gallon of milk. And lord knows, the criminals will be waiting.

It's 6:30 Sunday morning. Driving down the empty neighborhood streets, the homes look as slumbering as their occupants. Occasionally a person moves in the windows, sipping coffee, or someone is walking across a dew-covered lawn to fetch the newspaper. Overall, the scene is dark and silent as you head into downtown, passing by closed shops except for a convenience store and a donut shop. It is small-town America. What could possibly go wrong within this pastoral setting?

Not much except for the crazies in your head.

Pulling into the grocery store parking lot, there are ten cars, including yours. The lot is aglow in a lemony bath of halogen light as sunrise is still thirty minutes away. You wave hello to Mrs. Anderson, a longtime friend, who's entering the key code on her door to allow access into her car. There will now be nine cars. Surrounding this sparsely occupied lot is a small retail center (hair salon, art/framing gallery, and embroidery shop), and a plant nursery. Their parking lots are empty. Apart from the every-so-often annoying sound of a grocery cart's crippled wheels, what we have here is an area that is as quiet as a funeral.

You're driving a Honda CR-V, which happens to rank as one of the top ten least stolen vehicles in the country. In fact, your car includes some not-so-aesthetic features: rear bumper damage from a telephone pole; hood, roof, and trunk indentations from golf ball size hail; and a problematic rear view mirror that is adhered to the windshield with silver duct tape. Miscellaneous papers are scattered across the top of the dashboard, and a disorderly pile of clothing and running shoes make home on the back seat. It's a mess, but it gets you to where you need to go.

You park in a space that makes for a fifteen second walk to the store's entrance. As you get out, your golfing buddy Don Jenkins is exiting the store, carrying a watermelon.

"Seriously?" you call out, "6:30 in the morning and you're buying *that*?"

"A request from the misses," he says, then fumbles with his keys to unlock his 1984 Ford pickup. Once he leaves....eight cars in the parking lot.

Fifteen seconds is all it takes for you to enter the store. Such a contrast from the outside world. A bright florescent enclosure busy with stockers working the aisles, making sure the shelves are plentiful for the after-church crowds. It doesn't take but five strides into the store before the look of uncertainty drapes your face: *Did I lock my car?*

Did you lock your car at 6:30 on a Sunday morning in small-town America with eight cars in the parking lot? How did we ever get to this point? When I was a kid I would ride my bike into town and leave it leaning up against the side of the theater. Two hours later it'd still be there, untouched. From a criminal's mind you're driving one of the least cared about cars on the planet, and, to make matters worse, it's such a hail-plastered eye-sore, it screams, *NOT EVEN WORTH YOUR TIME AND HASSLE!!*

The other morning you went to the post office to mail a letter. Three cars were in the parking lot. All you needed was a stamp from the automated postage machine just inside the front door. Of course, you made sure you pressed that remote security anti-theft device first. When you finished (two minutes max) you drove away only to discover there was a second letter that you found on the passenger side floor. A U-turn took you right back to the post office. There were then only two cars. *Beep-beep!* You locked the car.

If there are no cars in the parking lot, we lock our cars. We go to a friend's house—we lock our cars. We go to a friend's house in the country—we lock our cars. After all, we never know when the next person to arrive will have a mischievous agenda. But we certainly suspect he's out there. Even Don Jenkins wasn't comfortable leaving his old and worn 1984 pickup unsecured in the near-empty parking lot. All he had to do was get a watermelon for the misses. A five minute errand at most. We are creatures of habit. He locked his truck.

Before the Sunday crowds descend upon the grocery store, the worshipers will have locked and unlocked their cars at church. Chances are every single person will have fallen victim to this habit. I find the church environment peculiar. It's the place where we go to lift ourselves, to reconcile, to understand, to have faith in mankind. Church parking lots themselves are like sanctuaries, as if the vehicles themselves are in prayer, and the unwritten creed is not to disturb them. No, they are not immune to theft, but if there's one place that's given plenty of space, it's the church.

In small towns, churches, plant nurseries, barber shops, hardware stores, post offices, and grocery stores rank as some of the top places to feel safe. Other than a matter of convenience that the remote security anti-theft device is in your hand, why lock your car in those places? I know, I know...it's going to feel like jumping off the high diving board at the swimming pool when you were eight-years-old— your belly stuffed full of high anxiety. I realize car theft and vandalism are a daily occurrence in this country, but it seems like we need to step outside of our discomfort zone and have a little faith in areas that aren't as risky, as a way to decondition our fears. After all, how are we even to begin having faith in mankind if we have to constantly lock our cars?

We have to start somewhere. I'm urging people to take road trips to small communities across the nation. Go to the local grocery stores with only two intentions: to NOT lock your car, and to buy a watermelon. And when you return to your car that will be in the same place you left it (and it won't have been tampered with), take that watermelon to the nearest city park, find yourself a picnic table under a tall shade tree, and have faith that your first cool, watery bite will indeed be the beginning of something remarkably and wonderfully unexpected.

Are You Serious?

The first time I went to New York City I was on business exhibiting my art at Art Expo International. It was late February and very cold. Everyone wore black. Black coats, scarves, pants, shoes, gloves, and hats. If someone wanted to really throw in a splash of color, then they'd jazz it up with a medium gray sweater or dark gray ear muffs.

And then there was me with my fire engine red, down-filled winter coat. Amongst all those people hustling about the sidewalks of Manhattan, bumping into one another, I stood out like a bleeding sore thumb. I might have been better off just wearing a giant bullseye. Street peddlers spotted me with ease, yelling from ridiculous distances, "Hey, you! Yeah you, Red! What's up, Red!? Gotta dollar!? Come on, Red, help me out." Red ignored them. Red pulled his red down-filled hoodie over his head as if that was a clever tactic to not be seen. But all it did was increase the full length of my redness. All those people dressed in attitude-black—they made no attempt to move out of my way. I turned my shoulders left and right, like I was avoiding incoming enemy missiles. I was the courteous guy from out of state, but also the clueless one who chose to wear red. I said, "Sorry," when I shoulder-bumped someone, but all they did was keep moving. By the end of the first day, I'd had it with New Yorkers.

My mother had tagged along for the three day drive from Texas to New York. All of my paintings and business supplies were fully packed in my van. Art Expo was held in the Jacob Javits Center—a gargantuan exhibit hall about the size of New York itself. Within a minute of exiting the Lincoln Tunnel, I quickly found myself navigating the notoriously crazy traffic snags and snarls of the city. Luckily, the Javits Center was just a few blocks away and I soon found myself parked and loading my art onto a dolly that I had brought. There were multiple signs along the unloading area that read, "UNATTENDED VEHICLES WILL BE TOWED!"

"Mom," I said, "Do not leave the van."

"Ok," she said.

I dollied a load of art work into the exhibit hall and went to the Exhibitor's Check-In table. I then went to my booth space (which seemed like walking the length of fifteen football fields), unloaded the dolly, and then headed back to the van, where I quickly discovered that my mother was gone. Nowhere to be seen. A uniformed worker was standing by my van.

"This your car?" he said as I approached.

"Yes."

"Well, I was 'bout to have it towed. You got lucky. Read the signs next time." His accent was southern, but his tone was northern. A transplanted New Yorker, but a New Yorker regardless.

"I'm sorry sir. My mother was here with the van, but she's disappeared."

As he went on to tell me how he had already had five cars towed that day, my vanishing mother reappeared, coming out of the Javits Center. "Mom," I said, "where did you go? You can't be walking off like that. This guy has unattended vehicles towed."

"I'm sorry, but I had to use the ladies room."

My mom said she *had* to go. Being cooped up in the car for three hours while driving, then waiting on me to return from my booth was pushing the limits of a full bladder. The uniformed worker didn't want to hear it. "Ma'am, you got lucky. I suggest next time you take care of your business before coming to unload your business. You lucky your van ain't towed." You could tell my mother wanted to bite him. She had that look of *"Just who are you!?"* Needless to say, she was not impressed with her first New Yorker encounter. And it didn't get any better when later that day I walked the streets in that bullseye, fire engine red winter coat. The both of us were off to a sour start in the Big Apple.

And then along came a bus.

It was a large metro bus plastered with ads for Broadway plays, Calvin Klein, and HBO. It was also a dirty bus that had seen plenty of hours rolling through the gray sloppy slush of street snow. The bus was one of several that made the continuous loop of transporting Art Expo exhibitors and attendees to their hotels, from 34th street (where the Javits was) up to 52nd and back. It was the third day of the five day show when my mother said she was going to spend part of the afternoon at the Guggenheim Museum.

"Mom," I said, "the Guggenheim is up around 90th Street. The show bus only goes so far as 52nd."

She said she had it all figured out and was going to take a taxi from that point on. I asked her if she was sure she wanted to tackle this little jaunt, being that this was New York City and she was about as familiar with it as she was the Arctic Circle. Without hesitation, she smiled and said, "I'll be fine." And off she went.

Right here is the part where I get to spoil this story's ending. This is where I get to brag about how New Yorkers really aren't so bad after all. It's how I came to look a little further beyond that perceived cold shell of the uniformed man who said we'd better stick with our van or it *will* be towed. I get to say, without a doubt, that the cliché "I Love New York" will never grow old. And for all those people who shouldered my red winter coat (including those street hecklers who yelled to see if Red could spare them a buck or two), to you guys I applaud your character. You are the pulse of the city. You are what makes New York what it is. You are hungry and loaded with charisma. You are cold. You are late and in a rush. You are real. And my understanding of all of this was sparked by one man: the damn best bus driver ever to drive on the face of this earth.

And then along came a bus…

By the time my mother's bus reached our hotel on 52nd Street, she was the only passenger left. As the bus approached the hotel she had an eerie sense that something wasn't quite right. The bus wasn't slowing down.

"Excuse me, sir," my mother had said to the driver, "but you just passed my hotel."

"Yes, ma'am, I did."

She looked out the window and noticed the street signs: 53rd Street...54th...55th.... "Sir, would you please stop this bus. You're going off of your route. I need to catch a taxi to go to..."

"Ma'am, I know where you're going. I heard you talking to the last passenger. So, here's what I want you to do: Sit back, relax, and enjoy the sights. My lunch break just started a few minutes ago and, ma'am, I am taking you to the Guggenheim."

"Are you serious? The Guggenheim is nearly 40 blocks away."

"Yes it is ma'am. Now just sit back and relax."

My mother would later tell me that he had a smile the width of the bus. She said she never saw it coming. She never could have predicted that this seemingly ordinary bus driver was what she would call "a diamond in the rough." She had encountered a lot of kind people in her life, but this guy threw a curve ball of greatness that came from out of nowhere. She offered to pay him, but he reluctantly refused it, asking only in return that she enjoy the museum. So, as she departed the bus, she kissed him on the cheek and said goodbye, never to see him again, but certainly never to forget him either. When she did finally catch a taxi to return to the Javits Center, she made it a point to say "Hi" to the uniformed worker who manned the front of the building and had told her she got lucky that my van didn't get towed. She told him she thought his accent sounded like he was from Tennessee. He said she was on the money, and it wasn't but a minute later they were talking of familiar names of small towns in the Smokey Mountains where she spent much of her childhood summers. They became instant friends.

And it wasn't but a few minutes after she talked to him, that she made her way into the exhibit hall and walked towards my booth. I can still see her now—full of anticipation to tell me how much she loved New York City. It was stamped on her face. A smile the width of a New York City bus.

Anyone Want To Go
Smell A Movie?

For several rotations, her head spins around three-hundred and sixty degrees. Her eyeballs are bulging, just shy of popping out of their sockets and being propelled across the bedroom. Lizard-like, her tongue moves in and out—a literal extension of the demonic presence that possesses her. She is twelve years old, and speaks in a guttural tone resembling the failing hydraulic system of a decrepit garbage truck. A biblical plague of locusts fly out of her mouth beneath a head of hair that is as well-kept as tornado debris. As the windows shatter, there is a burning hole in the wall behind her from which a thousand screaming ghostly souls are filling the room.

It could be the scene from a new horror film, or the scene from any horror film.

Today's horror flicks are becoming cookie cutter productions. How many times do we have to watch a screaming child claw at her bedroom floor as she zips backwards on her stomach in her nightgown? How many times do we have to watch her do a ninety-degree change in direction as she quickly slides backwards up a wall, only to be slammed against the ceiling where, at that moment, all eerie high-pitched violin sounds suddenly cease, and she drops to the floor with a heavy thud?

So often the same themes and scare tactics are repeated over and over without any thought of originality. *Into the dark basement our main actor goes. Lights out. Grab a flashlight. The camera pans the room slowly until an elderly woman is spotted through the spider webs. Her head is bent down with an entangled mess of grey hair falling in creepy disarray.* Will he survive the old woman's eminent chase up the stairs? Of course he will!—the movie still has an hour to go. But he'd better watch out for the man behind him in the bathroom mirror. You'll recognize his disfigured, hallowed-eyed face, as he's been making more bathroom mirror cameo appearances in horror films than there are Hollywood exorcisms.

If you want to horrify an audience, don't do it with "jump scares"—those sudden, unexpected surprises that completely catch people off-guard. Jump scares have a very short scare-life, after which, things quickly return to normal.

Horrification is a result of a few sinister seeds that must be planted deep within the cerebellum so they can creepily grow into something terrifying. A good horror film will rely more on pushing your psychological limits, rather than your exposure-to-gore limits. *A tap on her shoulder. A cold whisper in her ear. She turns to see who is there. Nobody. Just darkness. Until…another tap on her shoulder…* There's nothing jumping out at you, except your mind imagining what might be. When you're shuttering inside your head, that's when a horror film is paralyzingly successful.

However, since the movie industry is struggling to break free from cookie cutter horror films, then I propose we create a new genre of movies. A genre that will push the envelope of petrifying horror. A genre that will not just have the audience on the edge of their seats, but will send them…running for safety.

Enter: Foul Odor Horror movies.

These films will bring to the horror movie industry what horror movies have been missing. Just as Dolby Surround Sound has dramatically enhanced the movie goer's audible experience, then so too shall the latest technology enhance the sense of smell: Dolby Surround RealTimeStench.

And just what is RealTimeStench? It is created by:

- 8-cubic-yard commercial dumpsters that have been collecting garbage for at least ten years in the back alleys of restaurants that preferably discard unfinished meat dishes, blood-soaked Styrofoam meat packaging, meaty bone scraps, and raw chicken and turkey skins. These are specially selected dumpsters whose interiors are caked with years of spoiled meat grim, resulting in nothing less than housing the ghastly, putrid stench of bacterial breakdown.
- A commercial-grade gas furnace heating system designed to blow enough hot air to quickly fill a theater.

Theaters showing Foul Odor Horror films will utilize RealTimeStench systems by rigging the dumpsters upside down in the ceiling. They will be positioned so that their openings are flush with the ceiling, and hidden behind sliding panels. Air vents will be positioned inside of each dumpster to quickly deliver 92 degrees of foul, obnoxious, and repulsive dumpster air upon the movie patrons.

In addition to RealTimeStench, there are two major requirements to qualify as a Foul Odor Horror film:

1. It cannot be a horror film sequel. Originality is vital. The Exorcist was great. Should've stopped right there. The first Halloween was brilliant. Should've stopped right there.
2. The Foul Odor Horror genre will not use the typical horror movies titles that we've all grown accustomed to offering a lack of frightful originality. People know what to expect just from the titles (*Night of the Living Dead*, *The Texas Chainsaw Massacre*, *The Evil Dead*). Other Predictable horror film titles could be: *Rabid Sorority Girls Eat Planet Earth*, *Dead Teenagers Alive in the Sewer*, *Twenty Knives Stuck in the Bride's Eyes*, or *Blood-Sucking Snakes in the International Space Station*. Well, you've got a pretty good idea what's going to happen in those films. Foul Odor Horror films will have highly obscure titles to stir curiosity. Films slated

for the Christmas holiday season are: *Grandma's Teeth Rotted on the Subway, On Wednesday I Threw My Feet into the Boy Scout Campfire,* and *I Found Spoiled Meat and My Great Aunt Nelda in the Bloody Ice Cream.* Creepy. Strange. Unpredictable. Unsettling. Horrifying.

To give an example of a Foul Odor Horror film in action, and to see how RealTimeStench is incorporated, let's take a look at a scene from *Grandma's Teeth Rotted on the Subway*...

A grandmother is riding on a subway train and eating a rancid roast beef sandwich that she unearthed from her refrigerator where it had been in a plastic bag for over two years. Though the sandwich is dark-green, black, fuzzy, and completely unrecognizable, she nibbles away. This is because: a) she has severe cataracts, b) she has a rare nose condition where she is hard of smelling, and c) she's missing her tongue because in the first five minutes of the movie a street magician made it disappear (spoiler: the magician makes it reappear in the last five minutes of the film, just in time for her funeral. Oh, like that matters.)

Her back is to us as she eats. The camera slowly zooms in while moving around to her side. The sound of the train becomes less and less audible until it fades. In exchange, we now hear her saliva as she chews. It is the sound of gross. And gross becomes more and more evident as we are drawn closer to her mouth to witness the watery mucus secretions coating each bite, as well as a mouthful of rotted teeth. Through a series of quick flashbacks, and as the camera continues to zoom in, we learn she has a history of consuming spoiled sandwiches, night after night. Up close and way too personal, she opens her mouth to take in one last bite. Smiling as she does so, she exhales one enormous heavy breath directly at the audience...

The sliding panels in the ceiling have opened as, simultaneously, the gas furnace begins blowing the oppressive heat through the ventilation system. RealTimeStench is alive, fumigating every patron in the theater with a thick, warm blanket of foul dumpster stink...or, in this case, better known as Grandma's Breath.

Typically, four types of experiences shall occur as a result of being subjected to RealTimeStench:

1. The Survivors: These are the people who will make it through the rest of the film. There will be that initial reaction of "Good God, who farted!?" But other than that, they'll be back to eating their popcorn and enjoying the rest of the film.

2. The Sick: These poor souls will quickly be reaching for their air sickness bags located at each seat. Due to the high volume of retching that will be occurring, it is strongly suggested that everyone wear a plastic hair cap or rain poncho to prevent any undesirable splatter coming from patrons sitting behind you.

3. The Fainters: Chances are these people will miss the majority of the film. But no need to stress, as each theater will be assigned with a highly-trained Emergency Medical Team. These skilled first-responders will not interrupt the rest of the film.

4. The Runners: These people will just want out. And want out quickly! They'll be running for the exits to grab fresh air and a refund as soon as they can. They'll get the fresh air only. No refunds with a Foul Odor Horror film. That's part of the risk you take when you purchase a ticket to smell your movie.

So, there you have it. Unless the horror movie creators begin producing truly original and frightful films, then we're going to have to abandon that track, and move onto something a bit more different.

Even if it means raising a stink.

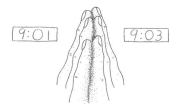

9:01

Baylee Almon would be 22 years old if she had attended my daughter's college basketball game yesterday. She would have watched her team get a proverbial spanking by Oklahoma Christian University. But she didn't watch it, because 21 years ago Baylee closed her eyes for the last time, soon after her rubble-coated body was in the rescuing clutch of a fireman's valiant arms.

You come to an opening that gives you full view of the memorial. Beneath you are 168 empty chairs. Beyond that is an expansive rectangular pool with just inches of shallow water. Positioned at opposite ends of the pool are two large walls referred to as the "Gates of Time". Each has an open entrance. On one wall, in large numbers above the entrance is the time 9:01. The other wall reads 9:03. It is then that you realize the one minute between the two walls harbors itself in the shallow serenity of the pool of water that was once N.W. Fifth Street in the heart of Oklahoma City. Within that one minute of 9:02, life was either taken or life was spared. By 9:03, the magnitude of the human spirit undertook the painful task of sifting through concrete, rebar, mangled steel, sheet rock, and too many personal belongings to remind us of who had perished.

You stand there looking down at the memorial. This body of water tugs on the gravity of your mournful thoughts that have billowed up so unexpectedly. It's 9:02AM on April 19, 1995. You were driving a UPS truck in Stonewall, Texas. On that warm, sunny morning you were standing in the doorway of a mobile home, waiting on a signature for a package. Then, you caught sight of the TV and joined in with millions of other viewers in disbelief at the destruction created by a cold-hearted, remorseless killer. For the remainder of the day, in that UPS truck, you drove around with your mind firmly planted in a place it would take 21 years to eventually see. And how would you know the effect the memorial would have on you? How could you possibly know the tears you would shed? 168 empty chairs honoring 168 people who had died. Of those, 19 smaller chairs to remember the deceased children. One chair was Baylee Almon's. Of course you would cry.

All you came to Oklahoma for was a basketball game. To watch your daughter and her team play about as miserably as they could possibly ever play. Amongst a sea of Oklahoma fans you had no choice but to listen to their loud, supportive cheering. That game clock could not tick fast enough to end this beat down, this proverbial spanking.

A day later, as you drove through Kansas for another collegiate game, you looked out at that wide-open, fertile landscape, and reflected on the pool of water between the Gates of Time. How insignificant did your daughter's poor three-point shooting now become. How insignificant was her team's embarrassing loss. If only Baylee Almon could be so blessed to have those problems. She would have happily missed every shot she would've taken, fully knowing she was alive. And the people in the stands would have no stories to tell regarding a tragic day in 1995.

But the stories do exist. And they all begin at 9:01.

A Fifth Third Confused

I love to ponder about the how's and why's of possibilities and impossibilities. I love to think about the quirky stuff that messes with my head. Like how it's impossible to squat down, put your hands under your feet, and lift yourself up off the ground. One of these days I'm going to figure that one out. I think about the impossibility of walking into a wall: If from you to the nearest wall there is a half-way point, and from that half-way point to the wall there is another half-way point, and so on and so on, then how is it possible if you have to always pass through half-way points that we are ever able to reach the wall?

And then there are the bigger ponderings.

How is it possible that there exists a banking institution, with branches in 12 states between Florida and Michigan, called the *Fifth Third Bank?* I mean, seriously, what kind of grammar is that? What if *Fifth Third Bank* opens up smaller, associated branches like the *Seventh Second Bank?* How many millions of confused looks will that one get? Or what if they raised the bar of perplexity to an entirely different level of confusion and created *Twelfth Sixth Tenth Eighth Bank?* It's a name-branding mess. I suggest the wannabe geniuses who came up with *Fifth Third Bank* admit their self-made catastrophe, and simply call it: *Bank.* After all, *Bank* is not even an official name of any bank. *"So, where do you do your banking?" "Bank."* For sure, I missed my calling as a corporate financial marketing consultant.

Imagine if *Fifth Third* decided to expand their corporate interests into entirely different markets...

Donut shops:

"Hello! Welcome to *Fifth Third One Half Dozen Donuts!*"

Fitness centers:

"At *Fourth-Twentieth Hour Fitness* we're committed to serving you every fourth of an hour twenty times a day!"

Convenience stores:

"At Seventh Eleventh we have a sixth beer of a pack on sale for $1/6."

Obscure enough to drive you crazy fifth-thirds of the time!

It's a name with historical roots, dating back to 1908 when *Third National Bank* and *Fifth National Bank* merged to become the *Fifth Third National Bank of Cincinnati*. From that point on, *Fifth Third* flexed its buying power and began acquiring and joint-venturing with many banks, firmly establishing themselves as a major regional financial contingent. The only problem is, nobody cares about how its name derived. All they're thinking (with a look on their face like they've sucked on a lemon) is: *Fifth Third*—it *sounds* weird. The term doesn't roll off the tongue, but rather stumbles awkwardly, tripping over your teeth, then helplessly sliding off your lips, before plummeting into your soup. Fifth Third. It's like someone said, *"To hell with making sense! We are steering this ship by our own illiterate rules!!"* And off they steered it, into a tidal wave of broken Englishness.

So, I'm thinking maybe, just maybe, *Fifth Third* is really part of the new math. Like a banking industry-only math. Perhaps you can only withdraw a fifth of your savings on the third day of the week. But then, why not just call it the *Fifth Tuesday Bank*?

Well, I'm deciding to conclude this story even though it's only a fifth done on my third attempt to making any sense of a bank that is not only a *Fifth Third*, but is apparently one and two-thirds of a bank as well.

HELP!!!

Fast, Easy Tech Support!

When my computer gives me an error message, I blurt out a few, barely audible, adolescent whimpers that are just short of crying. I also teeter on the brink of high anxiety knowing that my only recourse is to call for technical support, which means communicating with people 50,000 times smarter than me.

Like the erratic flight path of a butterfly, I scramble around the office in all directions looking for the little piece of paper where I jotted down the TurboBlast Tech Support website—the website designed to save my life. Flipping through manuals over here and digging through piles of post-it notes over there, I pray that I didn't toss it out. When, finally, I find it, I am only partially relieved because I know this is about as good as it's going to get. You see, the website only offers technical assistance through a live chat line. This means that I have to be able to make sense in typewritten words what my problem is, which is like the United Nations having a meeting without interpreters.

At the TurboBlast Tech Support web site home page everything looks so friendly and helpful. *Click here for fast, easy tech support!!! We look forward to serving you!!!*

They have no idea what is coming their way.

To log on to the Live Chat Support Service, I miraculously survive inputting my user name and password. To many, this may seem like such a simple task, but I will high-five myself as if I had just swum across a river of crocodiles.

Just short of a miracle, I actually make my live chat connection without a hitch. My on-line communication with a Technical Assistant commences with:

Please type your computer question here.

I begin like an idiot:

Me: Hello. How are you doing? Can I type my question now?
The tech's reply comes quickly.
Tech: Did you not read the question at the top of the page?
I'm already off to a bad start, but I keep my cool.
Me: Sorry. I tried to install the Xpress TurboBlast Software, but I keep getting a message that asks for an administrative name. What is my name?
Tech: You don't know your name?
Me: Of course I know my name.
Tech: Then why are you asking me what your name is?
Me: My administrative name. Do I use my name for that?
Tech: Yes, otherwise we'll be here all night.

I have talked to Tech Support now for forty-eight seconds, and I already feel like something just shy of a hemorrhoid. I type my name in the administrative field and click "OK". An error message quickly appears: "Invalid Entry". There's a wastebasket next to me that I kick against the wall, scaring the daylights out of Domino, our rat terrier, sleeping on the floor.

Me: It's not accepting my name.
Tech: Are you sure you spelled your name correctly?

Oh, my bad. I'm quite sure I misspelled my name. Pretty easy thing to do having spelled my name correctly for over HALF A CENTURY!!!

I check and notice that I have misspelled my name.

Looking down at Domino, I think about kicking him out the window. I'll just tell the kids that Domino was having a bad day. *The warning signs were undetectable. Had I known he was having issues, I would have had him see a canine psychotherapist. How was I to know he wanted to jump like that?*

I don't let the tech know of the misspelling, but simply say I fixed the problem. The next window that pops up asks for the software's serial number.

Me: It wants a serial number. Where is that?
Tech: It's on the back of the paper sleeve the CD was packed in.

The sleeve is next to me, but the serial numbers on the back are too tiny to read. I'm at the age just when things up close get a little fuzzy. Even the Toll House Chocolate Chip Cookie recipe on the back of the Nestle package is a challenge to read. *Pre-heat the oven to what? 350? 650? 850? Oh, who cares! Just broil the cookies!* Looking at the microscopic serial numbers on the back of the CD sleeve, you'd think I was squinting at a solar eclipse.

Me: The numbers are so small. How do you expect me to read them?
Tech: It shouldn't be that difficult.

It is that difficult. I tell Tech Support to please hold for a few minutes while I go find my glasses. A quick sprint throughout the house, poking my head in all the obvious places—it's a maddening hunt that results in nothing. They could be anywhere, but I'm pressed for time as I don't like to keep people waiting.

Back to the keyboard, I tell tech support I can't find my glasses.

Tech: Nothing can be done until you input your serial numbers. It's that simple. Is there someone else who can read it for you?

I should back my fingers off the keyboard, but they simply piano away, typing at will.

Me: Yeah, my great, great, cataract-infested, 95-year-old grandmother's in the room, picking corn out of her gums with a fork. You want her to read the numbers?
Tech: If she can, yes.
Me: That was a joke.

There's a pause. The tech's little cursor on the computer screen simply stays put, blinking on and off. For several minutes there is no answer. Just silence. I imagine seeing him or her parading around the office cubicles with a printout of our conversation. "Blind as a bat! Can't make out one digit of the serial number. I'm telling you, this dude is ooooold!" And the office erupts into a vibrant chorus of laughter. Champaign bottles are shaken and poured with bubbly wonderment over their heads. "Another ignorant customer has called in and we are the obligated souls who must drink our bellies full in remembrance of his idiotness! Drink, my fellow workers! Drink of merriment at the expense of this clueless goon!"
Just when I'm sure the tech's going to disconnect, there is typing once again.

Tech: I figured that was a joke, but I didn't want to take the chance that she might have really been in the room picking peas.
Me: It was corn.
Tech: None of that matters. You need the serial number. Do you understand?

"Do you understand?" Who are you, my mother? Mom? Is that really you? I must've been clobbered with over a thousand *Do you understand?*'s as a kid.

Me: I'm sorry, but the numbers are simply too small to read. Is there anything else we can do?

Tech: Let's try this. I'm going to need to link up to your computer with a service we provide called TurboBlast Remote Command. It will allow me to access your computer so that I can navigate its files and operating system just as you do there at home. If you don't mind, I will need your authorization to do so.

Me: Sounds like a plan, let's do it.

Tech: In a moment I will email you a link to open. Let me know when you've done that.

Moments later the link appears. After opening it, I follow several prompts that eventually lead me to where I need a password, which the tech provides.

Tech: I will be navigating within your computer. Please don't touch your cursor, as that will only interfere with my work.

A strange sense of vulnerability comes over me as I watch my pointer arrow move about my computer's monitor without my assistance. Whoever and wherever this tech is—could be Steve in Arizona, Raja in India, or John thirty miles down the road—he has complete control and I am completely fine with this because I know that I am a blithering moron when it comes to just about any computer task between the time I turn on and turn off the machine. In my opinion, every click of the mouse that doesn't result in some kind of error message is simply pure luck. Even surviving Spell Check is a miracle worthy of celebration. I must admit though, vulnerability aside, it is a deeply religious experience when a tech is navigating through your computer to solve a problem. A visceral euphoria comes over me as if I'm on the verge of being saved.

The tech has minimized the chat window to better view the multiple windows that pop-up. I can barely keep track of the pointer arrow. It's truly amazing the speed of the tech's work. Flawless. Absolutely flaw—*Oh, Dear God, no!*

The pointer arrow has stopped moving. Frozen. Frozen because I know the tech is currently in one of two states: shock or disgust, from having just viewed a picture of me in nothing but my underwear, standing up in the kitchen sink with two heads of iceberg lettuce, one under each armpit. On my stomach, and written with a neon pink marker, is a big, fat arrow that points towards my head. Beneath the arrow and just above the top of the underwear are the bright pink words, "The SINKing Three-Headed Monster!" It was the result of a lost bet at a Super Bowl party. And now, with the tech looking straight at me in the kitchen sink, I am at a loss for words.

Several more minutes of unbearable zero movement of the pointer arrow pass by until, at last, the tech expands the chat-line window and types a note:

Tech: Did you check the bathroom?
Me: Huh? For what?
Tech: Your glasses. Did you check the bathroom? Cabinets? Countertops? Drawers? Bedroom? Living Room? You really should have a designated place to keep them.

I am about to throw in the towel. My tech support has now turned into some sort of cyber space Dr. Phil/self-help/better-living consultant.

Me: I don't have time to look for the glasses, and I know they're not in the bathroom since I thoroughly cleaned it this morning.
Tech: We still can't rule out the kitchen.

No we can't. Nor can we rule out the oven, microwave, refrigerator, garbage disposal, or the cookie jar.

Me: Look, I don't know where the glasses are, and I really don't have time to look for them. Is there anything else we can do to speed things up?

Tech: Let's try this. I'm going to email you a link for you to automatically download the Xpress TurboBlast Software onto your computer. You'll be running smoothly in a matter of minutes. Okay?

I let out a huge sigh of relief. The kind you experience just when you think you're late for work, but it turns out its Saturday morning—your day off. I have been saved. My worries are over. I'm curious about who this tech is, so I ask, "Are you a man or woman?"

There is a long pause. The tech's reply cursor blinks idle. It just sits there blinking away time. Blink, blink, blink. Tic, tock, tic, tock... *Man or woman? Why did I ask that!?* But it's too late. The message was sent. This is like when you leave too long of a message on your girlfriend's phone recorder, and before you know it, irretrievable words spill out of your mouth, resulting in a huge pile of regret. Hoping to rectify the situation, you hang up, then immediately call back to smooth things out, but all that happens is another nightmare. Sort of goes like this:

"On that previous message, I didn't mean to imply that I didn't love you. I do. You're just the one. Oh, I don't mean that you're a 'just', like a 'sort of', but you're more than that. You're like that cute girl at the mall the other day who..."

Right there, you hear the inevitable "*Beep!*" followed by an automated voice: "This voice mail box is now full, please call back later." Any chance of explaining the similarity of the girl at the mall to her has now vanished. Best bet would be to grab your passport and fly far far away.

The tech still has not responded. This is getting too uncomfortable and weird, but I continue typing.

Me: I didn't mean the man or woman thing. Sex doesn't matter to me. I mean your sex. I mean—(*Enter*)

Hitting *Enter* was a mistake. I fire off two quick apologies for anything and everything—trying my best to explain that by "sex" I meant "gender" but no reply comes back. By the look on my face, you would think that either I was being hypnotized or that I had just witnessed something horribly bizarre, like a group of clowns flogging a man selling yellow smiley buttons. Suddenly, the tech's reply appears, and it is as unforgiving and bleak as any I could dream up. It comes in the form of six depressing words:

Your Tech Support session is terminated.

Well, I guess I'm on my own. Life has been pretty good up to this point. Birth went all right. Loved playing baseball when I was nine. Had a riot skipping rocks across the pond at age twelve. And who could ever forget the time when I was eighteen and a friend and I went to the local grocery store and bowled down Coke bottles with cantaloupes in Aisle 3. Beyond that, all else was pretty much smooth sailing, except for one wee little slip of the tongue with tech support.

But you know, I'm going to get over this. I'm going to build myself a new day and move forward! I head to the kitchen for some cookies and milk. After all, food is that which has a way of replenishing the soul, and Lord knows I need it. Once there, my hand dives into the cookie jar and...well, well, well...maybe I'm being given a second chance, but surprise of all surprises, I pull out my glasses.

Express TurboBlast Software, here I come!

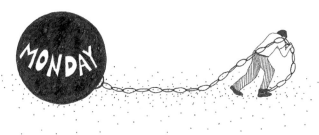

Fixing Monday

Monday.

The word alone evokes images of too little sleep, headaches, sluggish commutes, and endless cups of black coffee.

As your bloodshot eyes struggle to open, Monday has already reared its ugly head at your bedside. Its heavy face stares at you with ten thousand pounds of annoyance. Its breath is burdensome with a putrid odor keeping you from falling back to sleep. At 5:00AM, Monday already stinks.

Arriving to work, you notice there is not one single co-worker who has dodged the wrath of Monday. As they shuffle around with a head-filled quagmire of drudgery, their enthusiasm is at another all-time low. Seventy-two hours ago they had a bounce in their step and were thrilled to be alive. TGIF is not just a welcome cliché, but is also the celebratory creed of the working world. Rain or shine, the long awaited weekend never fails to deliver relief. Of course, they push Sunday to its limits, trying to squeeze out every drop of its restoring tonic. They have a little more to eat, a little more to drink. And then they go to bed late, doing whatever they can to not think about the forthcoming and menacing buzz of the alarm clock.

If you find that you're missing some screws or hex nuts as you assemble your IKEA furniture, you can bet that the packing error occurred on a Monday. If your cable man is supposed to be at your house on Monday, don't expect him until Tuesday. If you're supposed to have brain surgery on a Monday...cancel it!

It is a day that needs to be restructured. Twenty-four hours is too many hours for a Monday. I propose we make Monday a 12-hour day, and give 36 hours to Sunday. The fact is Sunday goes by too quickly. If you'll watch the clock closely on Sunday, what you'll see is that one minute is up in thirty seconds. In fact, late into Sunday night, it takes only twelve seconds for a minute to pass by. Unbeknownst to many, Einstein discovered this Theory of Time Rip-Off Relativity by applying his advanced mathematics: $E=MC^2$ (where E represents No Energy, M is Monday, and C^2 is Crappy Crappy. Hence: No energy on a crappy crappy Monday). He had great intentions to publish his findings which occurred on a Sunday night. Unfortunately, the following Monday morning he took his hand-written papers to a publisher who had a head-busting hangover. The combination of his post-intoxicated state and having to rise early for work led to his frazzled mind mistaking the papers as linings for a kitty litter box. Needless to say, they perished.

Still, it really doesn't take Einsteinian theory to prove that Monday's hours need to be curtailed. If we allot 36 hours to Sunday, then that means Monday morning would roll around at the regular Monday noon time—no more dark, dreary mornings. Instead of an 8-hour work day, Monday would now have a 4-hour work day. That alone would make people look forward to Monday. There would now be a 36 hour work week. With the decrease in on-the-job errors, that alone will generate bonuses to be paid out for increased worker productivity. Everybody wins.

The assembly pieces to your IKEA furniture...they'll all be there. Your cable TV will be working by Monday afternoon. And that brain surgery you have scheduled...it's a no brainer...go for it!

The Tree

I was getting ready to swim at the city pool, when I noticed a little girl in a stroller. She was parked next to her grandmother who was sitting on a bench. The girl's sister was in the pool practicing with a swim team. It was a perfectly normal setting, with one exception— what she was doing with her hands. She was tapping, scrolling, swiping, and expanding the screen of an iPad.

Or perhaps this was normal—the new normal. I can remember when cell phones first hit the market, and how astonished we were when learning someone had bought an iPhone for their 8th grader. *Seriously!!!??* And now, twelve years later, you'd be hard-pressed to find a 6th grader who doesn't have one.

I was amazed by this little girl in the stroller—her fingers nimbly operating the iPad.

"How old is she?" I said to the grandmother.

"She's—"

The girl beat her to the answer by quickly punching two fingers into the air. I had to chuckle at this inaudible interjection, as I was fascinated by the immediacy of her emphatic sign language. There was almost something mature about her action.

"You're two years old?"

She looked up at me with a smile and said, "Yep!" Not just a two-year-old yep, but a confident yep—a confidence that showed in the way she adeptly worked the iPad. And as unbelievable as it may seem, she displayed something that comes with the air of confidence: the telltale signs of impatience when the iPad's internet connection responded slowly to her touch.

Two years old. How quickly they learn. How quickly they master. And so easily distracted. She should be watching her sister swim. There was an engagement that was missing. The well-crafted lure of technology had stolen her attention. The spray of water from the swimmers' flip turns that occasionally hit her bare feet, and the coach's raised voice giving instructions to the busy swim lanes did not deter her attention in the least. At two years of age, she made me wonder about the future...

*   *   *

"Mommy...what's wrong with it?" said the five-year-old girl, pointing upwards at a large tree. "It doesn't do anything."

"What do you mean it doesn't do anything?" Replied the mother, kneeling next to her.

"I swiped it. Nothing happened."

"Oh, that's because this is a real tree. Out here in the park things are different. This tree not only provides shade, but it's a place for animals and insects to live."

"The trees in our backyard don't have bugs or animals?"

"No," said the mother, putting her arm around the girl's shoulders. "Our trees are iTrees. They're different. They're interactive smart trees. You can learn everything about nature from an iTree's trunk touch screen."

"But no bugs or animals?"

"On the trunk screens, yes."

The girl looked at her mom with a perplexed face. "But no real ones, right?"

The mother paused for just a moment, then said, "Yes, that's right."

"But why?"

Turning her daughter so they were face to face, the mother put her hands on the girl's shoulders, then said, "Because iTrees use the latest technology. Nothing provides as much information. And nothing entertains you like an iTree."

She went on to tell her daughter about the iTree's Labyrinth Limb System, a technological breakthrough that bore edible, imitation hybrid fruits. LLS did this through a conversion process whereby 3D imagery became 3D Sculpt—the quantum next step beyond virtual reality. "In fact," said the mother. "We'll have our first non-pollinated fruit soon, after ArborTech installs our Apple iTree next week."

As her mom continued, speaking far beyond her daughter's grasp, the girl's attention waned when she spotted a blue jay flying overhead, then disappearing inside the tree's canopy. "Our iTrees don't have birds," she said.

"That's true," replied her mother. "But they're working on that. It's only a matter of time until they figure out the necessary technology to attract them. Let's be thankful the trunk touch screens can tell us anything and everything about birds."

The mother stood up and took her daughter's hand, telling her it was time they headed back home. But there was a slight resistance as the daughter pulled back. "Look, mommy! Look!" A second blue jay flew into the canopy, and moments later the two birds could be seen, apparently dancing in flight as they sprang in and out of the tree.

"They're playing. Possibly courting," said the mother.

"Courting?"

"Yes, like they've found each other. Like love."

"Ha!" The girl laughed. "Like love birds!"

The girl slipped from her mother's grasp, and walked up to the tree, where she reached out and let her small fingers travel along the rugged crevices of the tree's bark. Her nails skimmed through and collected fragments of small patches of soft, verdant moss protruding from the wood. Traveling up along the trunk, she saw two ants, a beetle, and three ladybugs. "Mom, where are these bugs going?"

Her mom walked up next to her. "I'm not sure. I suppose looking for food. Let's go home and ask the iTree."

She grabbed her daughter's hand, but she resisted again, then slipped free. "Honey, we should really be getting home. It'll be dark soon. And you know how pretty the iTrees glow at night."

"Mom, do you think they'll marry?"

"Will who marry?"

"Them." Her daughter pointed at the two blue jays continuing their flight dance.

"Silly. You know birds don't marry."

"Do the iTrees know it?"

"I seriously doubt there's any information about birds getting married."

"So iTrees don't know everything. They don't tell you about birds in love either, do they?"

"Well....no, you're right." The mother looked up into the tree's canopy, as a small cluster of leaves fell towards her. She extended her arms, then cupping her hands in hopes to catch one, and caught two. She sandwiched the leaves together and gently massaged them between her thumb and index finger. They were textured and firm; fresh off the vine, so to speak. Above her, the blue jays chirped in their playful chase.

Her daughter took her other hand and placed it on the tree's trunk. "Mommy, feel how rough the tree is." The girl pressed her nose against the bark and took a deep whiff. "Smell it, mommy...it smells nice."

Her mother did just that, closing her eyes as she inhaled—the aroma of a moist forest. When was the last time she had smelled this? When was the last time she had roamed in the woods? Years? Decades? Yet how quickly her memory recalled the tree's scent. Experience, she thought. It was everything. The iTree was smart, but could not relate to experience. It couldn't evoke the feeling a child gets watching two birds dancing in love. It couldn't capture the essence of a moment.

She looked down at her daughter who was watching a ladybug

crawl on the tip of her finger, her eyes full of fascination. "Honey," she said. "My mother once told me about a time when I was a little girl. She said I was about two-years-old when I was at my sister's swim practice."

"Aunt Jessie was a swimmer?"

"Yes she was. And a good one at that."

"That must've been neat watching her swim."

"Well that's the point of my story. For so long, I really never watched her much. My mother said I was always playing games on my iPad, which was a big clunky computer-like device they had back then. Anyway, she said one day she took it out of my hands and said 'No more' with it. That I needed to watch my sister swim. She said I wasn't the one to blame, but rather it was she who gave me the iPad to keep me occupied. She said it was a big mistake on her part, that I wasn't noticing what matters."

With slightly squinted eyes, her daughter tilted her head and asked, "What matters?"

There was a brief pause as she looked at her daughter whose attention was back on the ladybug, watching it now crawl up her arm. Her mother cracked a smile and said, "What matters...is this tree."

"But mom, you said it's getting late. Shouldn't we go now?"

Her mother's smile widened a bit more. "No," she said. "I think we're perfectly fine right here."

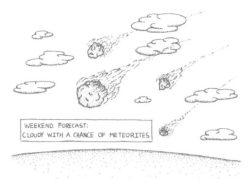

WEEKEND FORECAST:
CLOUDY WITH A CHANCE OF METEORITES.

The Lot

There was a time when weather forecasters were called weathermen. But, as women entered that industry's workforce, the occupation's title no longer worked, so a change was needed. And that's where I get curious…

Why are meteorologists called meteorologists? Why aren't they called weatherologists? Biologists study biology. Physiologists study physiology. Psychologists study psychology. It would certainly seem logical that meteorologists would study meteors. But they don't.

The weather forecasting industry snagged the meteorologist name first, leaving the real meteor scientists with "meteoriticist." Takes me about four times to finally pronounce it correctly. And even then, I sound like I'm calling someone a "meteorite racist." "HEY, YOU!!! YOU'RE NOTHING BUT A BIG FLYING SPACE ROCK HATER!!!"

I mean, if there was a choice to decide between weatherologist or meteorologist, how difficult could it have been? I can only imagine the weather forecasting powers-that-be, formulating the identity of their industry as they sat around a solid oak conference table in their think-tank room...

Genius #1: "These people who will study and forecast the weather...just what shall we call them?"

Genius #2: "Weather trolls?"

There are 18 geniuses in the room. (Yes, it's a very big table.) None of them chuckle at weather trolls, as they discuss its possibilities. Except for genius #9. He gives it a big thumbs down, but is immediately swatted on the top of the head by genius #10 (who, by the way, is a much larger genius).

Genius #9: "What was that for!!?"

Genius #10: "You're acting like a child."

Genius #9: "I'm acting like a...we're discussing 'weather trolls', and I'm acting like a child? Seriously...weather trolls!?"

Genius #1: "Alright #9, calm down. Any other suggestions?"

Genius #4: "Weather puppets."

Genius #9 stands up and shouts, "THIS IS THEEEEEE MOST ASININE MEETING IN THE HISTORY OF CIVILIZATION!!!!" As genius #10 raises his hand, threatening to swat again, #9 cowers in silence.

Other geniuses give more ideas...

"Weather cops"

"Storm wolves"

"Masters of Prediction"

"Humidity hounds"

"Climate clowns"

Genius #9: "Who the hell suggested 'climate clowns'? #4 was that you again?"

#4 proudly raises his hand and nods.

Genius #1: "Perhaps, #9, you have a better suggestion than those already proposed?"

Genius #9: "I do have a better one."

Genius #1: "Which is...?"

Genius #9: "Weatherologist."

Genius #10: "That does it!! Enough of your smart mouth!!"

#10 yanks #9 up out of his seat, then puts him in a headlock before delivering five stinging swats and a scalp-burrowing knuckle rub.

Genius #1: "Weatherologist!!? WEATHEROLOGIST!!!!? #9 this is preposterous!!! Out to The Lot!!!"

Genius #9: "Noooooo!!! Not The Lot!! Please, I beg of you!!"

It is all too late. #10 grabs him by the shirt collar and, with the assistance of four other geniuses, he is escorted down a long hallway to the front glass doors of the building. There, he looks out at the cold, snowy January day where a sharp wind cuts through some barren trees. Genius #1 walks up to his side and hands him a snow shovel.

Genius #1: "You know the rule: Act like a child, pay the price."

Genius #9: "Seriously, sir...you guys were actually discussing weather troll as a possibility? Was weatherologist really that bad of an idea? I mean, seems like the obvious choice to me."

Genius #1: "Preposterous!"

Out the doors he went while they threw his coat and gloves at him. He and the 17 others had been called to the emergency meeting on a Sunday morning. The building was normally closed on the weekends. But on this particular day, the geniuses had convened to make history by name-branding the weather specialists.

The Lot—the building's parking lot was covered with ten inches of snow. It would take #9 the rest of the day to shovel it. If he declined the job, he would forever be stripped of his genius status. And that, he knew, was simply not worth it. After all, he'd been in this situation before, when, in the spring, he had to mow the perimeter lawns. *Weather trolls. Climate clowns. Good lord, what will they ever think of next?*

As #9 shoveled into the night, the geniuses settled into the trenches of their marathon meeting, deliberating over more identity suggestions. "Storm troopers" was at the top of the list, until genius #1 mentioned it might have a slight copyright conflict with Star Wars.

Genius #4: "Then what about Darth troopers?"

Genius #1: "Darth troopers? Are you serious? I mean that has nothing to do with anything. That doesn't even make Star Wars sense. #4 you're getting real close to a snow shovel."

Genius #10: "Shall I swat him?"

Genius #1: "No, not yet. But what you can do is give me a winning suggestion. No one's going home until we finish what we set out to do."

As another hour rolled by, appetites grew, and pizza was delivered. Crusts were tossed out to Genius #9, who was nearing completion of his back-breaking punishment. It was customary to be fed like a dog when working The Lot.

Gnawing on a crust with the hint of pepperoni, he saw a streak of light cut across the night sky. He knew shooting stars were more common in the summer months, so it was a bit of a surprise. *Could this be a sign?*

And then it hit him: *Meteor!!* He quickly finished his last few feet of shoveling, then ran inside the building to rejoin the meeting....

Genius #1: "Welcome back #9. Finish the job?"

Genius #9: "Yes, sir. And thank you so much for the table scraps. Delectable."

Genius #1: "Do I detect a hint of unnecessary childish sarcasm?"

Genius #9: "My apologies. Sir, if I may...I have a revelation to share with the group. I believe I have a worthy identity suggestion."

Genius #1: "Then proceed."

Genius #9: "Let me ask all of you: What single force of nature has the ability to alter the Earth's weather patterns? And I'm talking about a global scale."

Genius #4: "Hurricanes?"

Genius #9: "Nope."

Genius #10: "Such a stupid question. Blizzards."

Genius #1: "Blizzards? Global blizzards? How might that be possible #10?"

Genius #10: "I dunno."

Genius #1: "You know #10, sometimes I really wonder how you ever achieved genius status. I swear you've got a lot more brawn than brains."

#9 couldn't help but smile at this little beating #10 was finally getting.

Genius #1: "Ok, # 9...cut to the chase. Enlighten me."

Genius #9: "Meteors, sir. A giant meteor could generate global climatic changes. And only one person could forecast it all. Get where I'm going with this?"

Genius #1: "Are you suggesting...meteorologist?"

Genius #9: "Yes I am, sir."

Genius #10: "He's an idiot!"

Genius #1: "He's a GENIUS!!!"

Genius #10: "WHAT!!!?"

Genius #1: "Absolute genius!! And you #10, you big thug....to The Lot!! All that snow #9 shoveled—I want it back where it came from!"

It would take #10 well into the early morning hours in order to finish the unprecedented job of putting the snow back from where it had previously been shoveled. Not long after he was sent outside, the remaining geniuses had voted unanimously to go with "meteorologist" as the title to call anyone who studied or forecasted the weather. Of course, Genius #4 strongly suggested they vote for "meteorologist Darth trooper dude"—a suggestion that caused Genius #1 to lose his patience, sending #4 out to The Lot as well.

Genius #1: "It's hard to find good geniuses anymore."

Genius #9: "Well, I'm glad I could help."

Genius #1: "And to think that you actually considered weatherologist as a possibility."

Genius #9: "Yeah, just what was I thinking?"

Living In The Moment

So that you don't get your hopes up, let it be known that my daughter did not get the puppy.

Now, let's begin…

Bailey is a sophomore at St. Edwards University, where she's a shooting guard on the basketball team. She was recruited for various reasons: ball handling, a high basketball IQ, game swagger, and she can drain 3s from downtown.

It's a sweet sight watching your daughter's 3-point shot sail through the air with such accuracy that you can predict the oncoming swish solely based on its trajectory. But even sweeter is when she plays for Division II St. Edwards and her opponent is Division I Texas State University, and that 3-point shot rains down with victorious redemption. After all, she didn't return to Texas State's home court just to put on another 0 11 shooting performance like she did the year before. Besides, this was her hometown, and she was determined to not let people walk away with another memory like *that one*. After she made the game's opening basket, she began positioning herself beyond the arc and sank three 3s. One shot in particular was a quick release that she nailed after a stare-down into the eyes of her defender. The ball appeared to cradle itself in the net---a perfect swish that silenced the home crowd.

After St. Edwards' opening 10-0 lead, the closest Texas State would come was nine points. Midway through the fourth quarter, the

Hilltoppers led the Bobcats by 20. In the end, it was St. Edwards upsetting Texas State for the first time in school history, 65-51.

The stars were lined up for Bailey. So many parts of the game were markers of success, and would solidify themselves as everlasting memories for her. As a parent, and being someone who had played basketball for a large part of my life, I lived vicariously through the game. I felt just as much a part of the victory as she did. Of course, her team could have lost to Texas State, and I would still be the proud father as I am at all of her games. Pride isn't easily removed after you've coached your daughter since she was a 5-year-old.

I envisioned her riding on the bus back to Austin---celebrating the defeat of a Division I opponent. Bodies bouncing in their seats to the catchy rhythms of hip-hop. These kind of victories don't come often. What else could possibly be on her mind? I texted her to say congratulations.

Me: What a game! You played great!

Bailey: Thanks.

Me: Your three ball was on. That must have felt so good, especially on Texas State's home court.

Bailey: It was pretty awesome.

She sent another text directly after that one. It was accompanied with the photo of a puppy.

Bailey: Will you get him for me for Christmas?

Me: The puppy's for sale?

Bailey: Yeah! My friend's mom is selling him. Isn't he cuuuuuute!!!?

Was I missing something here? Was there a gap in time that I had skipped over? Was Einstein's theory of general relativity at work? Could this be the first ever "telephonic wormhole" whereby our conversation entered a shortcut in a space-time continuum, and all permanent basketball dialogue had been sucked into oblivion? Thirty minutes ago she had quite possibly experienced the biggest victory of her collegiate career, but now she was asking about a puppy? I wanted to talk about the two steals she made, the offensive charge she took, and her invaluable shooting contributions. It was time for a phone call. She answered with instant enthusiasm.

"Can we get the puppy? Isn't he cuuuuuute!!? Pleeease, Dad, can we?"

"Bailey, you're in college."

"Isn't he cuuuuuute!!?"

"Bailey, you're---"

"He's adooorrrable!!"

I had to speak quickly or I was neeeeeever going to get a word in.

"You're a college student. You'd see the puppy only on the weekends. We'd be the ones raising it."

"The puppy's a he, not an it," she said assertively.

"Okay, a he. You wouldn't see him much."

"But he's adooorrrable!!"

"Yes, he is. I can't deny that. But, Bay, if you're going to get a dog, then that dog needs to bond with you. Seeing him only on the weekends isn't going to cut it. Wait till after college before you get one."

It was the first quiet of our conversation. I imagined our local newspaper's game coverage headline: ST. EDWARDS UPSETS STATE. BUT PUPPY HAS NO CHANCE. FATHER KILLS MOMENT. "There he is!!!!!!!" the townsfolk would angrily yell, brandishing battle axes and torches to guide them into the night. "The puppy hater!!! Do not let him flee!!! Off with his head!!! He is no father!!! He is but evil's rot!!!"

"Bay, am I making any sense?"

The excitement had drained from her voice. She had conceded to my suggestion. "Okay," she said. "I guess I see your point."

Before we hung up, a curiosity loomed in my mind. "I got a question. This game that you just played, this incredible win---are you excited about it?"

"Of course I am, why?"

"Oh, I don't know. Guess I'm just a little surprised about the puppy."

"What about the puppy?"

"Well, that you're mentioning him like the game didn't even happen."

"Dad, it was a great game, but it's over. I mean, yeah it was a huge win, but...isn't he soooo adooorrrable!!?"

Our conversation ended soon after. I couldn't help but smile as I now understood the simplicity of her mindset. The game was over. She had given it her full attention. There was no puppy out there on the court, nor part of any discussion on the bench or in the locker room. But on the bus ride home, as they shared the highlights of the game, the normalcy of their lives returned. Snapchat, Twitter, music, homework, life's dramas, what to eat, and a puppy all surfaced amongst their discussions.

Here I was though, talking to my daughter whom I had coached in basketball leagues and tournaments for so many years. My mind was cemented in a vicarious state. I wanted to talk at length about nothing more than the memorable details of the upset over Texas State. This kind of victory doesn't come often.

And neither did those moments with your daughter, when---little did she know---she inadvertently taught you that there's really only one thing sweeter than victory...

Living in the moment.

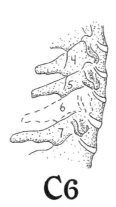

C6

My plan was to run him until he dropped. No breaks. Just gradually increase his pace until his tank ran out. I wanted to see how much endurance strength he had. Unfortunately for me, I never discovered it. There was one slight glitch in my plan that I hadn't foreseen…the kid just kept on running.

*   *   *

I often thought that Lee Bryant's energy should've been harnessed as an alternative fuel source. He simply had no stop button. Rest was a four-letter word he preferred not to hear.

We would meet two to three times a week at a college intramural field. There, beneath the lights on warm Texas summer nights, Lee let loose, clipping along at speeds that didn't slow down. He was 15 years old, and my job was to prepare him for his upcoming high school basketball season. To build up his aerobic conditioning required on the court.

For two years I ran Lee.

Until I couldn't.

*   *   *

September 18, 2010.

The light pole stood tall and solid in the Target parking lot. Its sole purpose was to illuminate. Beyond that, it was completely unforgiving.

Lee was 19 years old. He had just exited the store with a couple of items, and was getting into his car, preparing to drive away. Fifteen minutes was all it would take for him to walk through the front door, before going directly into the kitchen to raid the fridge for a quick snack. In seventeen minutes he'd be chilling in his room, watching ESPN. In twenty minutes, he'd be back at the fridge, rummaging for anything to appease his high metabolic rate.

Unfortunately, not only did his car not travel more than thirty seconds from the moment he left the parking space, but he also never made it home that night. And one light pole had changed everything.

While one hand was trying to call his mother with a cell phone, the other was attempting to secure his seatbelt. His eyes were anywhere except paying attention to where the car was going, which was being steered with his knee. Inadvertently, Lee had put himself in a very vulnerable and precarious situation.

At 15 mph, his car aimlessly ran nose-first into the concrete base of the light pole. At the moment of impact, Lee's head was turned to the right as he dealt with the seatbelt. This would be the last time in the foreseeable future---and possibly his life---that he would ever be able to grab something, and one airbag had made certain of that.

He was completely caught off-guard when the airbag deployed, forcing his neck to bend at a bad angle. Less than a second later, much of his body was paralyzed. It comes with the territory when the sixth cervical vertebrae shatters into small fragments, resulting in a damaged spinal cord.

But there was a moment after the impact when Lee had no idea that paralysis had even occurred. For all he knew, this was nothing more than a little one-vehicle accident, and he might as well get out of the car to assess the damage. He shifted his torso to the left and tried to unlock his door.

Tried. It's fair to say he didn't even make that much progress. It was bad enough that he couldn't move his arms, but the real horror was the fact that neither could he move his fingers, legs, and feet. They were completely limp.

He had felt nothing as C6 shattered. No pain of any kind, just an unwelcome numbness. There would be no unlocking the door at the request of the person outside his car---the same person who was calling 9-1-1. As Lee sat there, waiting for the paramedics and police to arrive, he had but one thought: "Shit! Shit! Shit! This can't be good...this can't be good."

Soon he would hear the sirens of the emergency vehicles. And soon a police officer would be telling Lee to remain calm---they would be getting him out. That's when he heard the sound of breaking glass as his rear windshield was being smashed open.

∗ ∗ ∗

A few hours later, in the ER at Brackenridge Hospital in Austin, Lee was wearing a cervical neck brace as he laid prone on a gurney. He was waiting for a doctor to give him the results from his MRI. "Basically, your sixth vertebrae is missing. It's shattered, and highly unlikely that you'll ever walk again."

In Lee's words: "That's when the waterworks hit."

At this point, authorities were attempting to contact Lee's parents and sister. He was alone, and some of the worst news possible had just been delivered to him. It's a tough situation when you're a teenager and you learn that three-quarters of your body has basically been permanently anesthetized. Your entire life has evolved around sports. There's no telling how many tens of thousands of miles your legs have run. And you always hated the word "rest" because it meant being idle, and idle just sucks. Long before your youth Little League Baseball days, you thrived on high-energy movement. And now...

An airbag knocked C6 clear out of the line-up.

"We're prepping for surgery," said the doctor. "You've got vertebrae fragments scattered around that need to be cleaned up. We're also going to fuse C5 and C7 together with a titanium piece. It's critical we do this now so that the spinal cord isn't subjected to any more damage."

Through his watery eyes, Lee nodded in agreement. Soon after, he was wheeled into the OR.

*   *   *

Life is what it is, and sometimes you're a lot better off joining it, rather than lamenting over it, or fighting it. That's how Lee saw it, anyway. And this became immediately clear as soon as he came to from the surgery, when a sense of hope encompassed him. The road ahead wasn't going to be easy, but at least he had a road. And if the only means of getting around is in a wheelchair, then so be it. It's a highly admirable attitude, given the range of his disabilities: paralyzed chest down, partial upper arm muscle deficits, unable to move fingers, no abdominal contractions, unable to yell because his diaphragm can't contract, inability to maintain body temperature, and an inability to sweat.

Much of his acceptance of his "new normal" came from spending a month at TIRR in Houston, which is one of the world's most respected and aggressive spinal cord injury rehab centers. There, he saw just how alone he wasn't. He met numerous 20-year-olds who had been in vehicle or water-related accidents, such as diving head-first into dark, shallow rivers. The higher up on the spine the injury is, the more severe the limitations. C1 and C2 injuries were the worst: complete paralysis of arms and legs, limited head and neck movement, trouble breathing without assistance, and ability to speak sometimes impaired. There, in his wheelchair, as a therapist tied his shoes, how fortunate Lee felt to be able to freely move his arms. How lucky he felt to be able to drop his limp fingers onto a computer keyboard and type a college essay or search the web.

"It's the putting on the socks that sucks," he says. 'I can't do it. With those, I need help. And jeans…well, I can put them on, but they just take fiveever."

Fiveever. It's his own little neologism that describes the act of doing something taking longer than forever. Or, as we might hear phonetically…*four*ever.

"I'm good," he says. "I've accepted this life and do what I can do. I'm attending classes at *Texas State University*, working on a degree in Therapeutic Recreation, and that's a big deal to me. I hope for two things: to work in a spinal rehab center, and that my disability will improve. You have to have hope. I mean, why not? Look at technology. It's way on my side as there are cars out there that are designed so I can drive. So, yeah, as a whole, I'm good."

And that's where I come in…into his room. For the past six years, I've been training him there, doing whatever I can to build strength in whatever areas possible. He has a pair of special gloves that allow him to hold onto barbells and dumbbells. I also have him pull on elastic cords in all directions, as well as have him work with a medicine ball that he catches and throws with the heels of his hands.

No, we're not running sprints on the intramural field anymore. To train Lee for aerobic conditioning is certainly out of the question. And as for basketball…will Lee ever shoot one again? What are the chances? Many would say slim to none. But never say never, as his workouts are not just to build and maintain strength, but to hopefully wake up a nerve somewhere---to fire up a neuron that'll send a long-awaited signal to the brain that says, "Hey, remember me? I'm alive!"

Watch Over You

I t was the day after Christmas, and my car was the only one in the parking lot. Morning light was just arriving as I sat on a curb to tie my running shoes. I had my iPod playing "Watch Over You" by Alter Bridge. The song moves you in so many ways, and I have listened to it more than any other song in my collection of over a thousand. My intent was to run four miles with nothing but Alter Bridge cranked up. An easy run with only the music on my mind.

I think I ran ten strides before I stopped, turned around, and walked back to the car to put my iPod away. I have no idea why I did that. Though later, I did wonder.

*   *   *

I took the trail along the river that cuts through town. I was not just the lone runner, but was the only person to be seen. Three sounds could be heard: the crunch of the gravel beneath my feet, birds in the trees, and my breathing. Eventually, the trail turned and took me away from the river, leading to a long straightaway that ran adjacent to a street. On my left was a baseball complex, and on my right was a neighborhood. It was there that I heard the fourth sound. A woman's voice.

"Excuse me....excuse me," she said from across the street. Her voice was weak and sounded desperate. She was in her mid-30s and was pushing a two-seat baby stroller. As I crossed the street, I watched her wipe some tears off her cheeks.

"You okay?" I asked. The stroller was occupied with an infant and a child no more than two-years-old.

"I need to get to Siesta Mobile Home Park. Do you know where that is?"

I used to be a UPS driver in my town. There's not a street I don't know. "That's over on Uhland road," I said. "Kinda far from here."

"How far?"

"At least two miles."

Her face dropped. She was exhausted. I suspected she had come from the nearby bus station. Perhaps she hadn't slept much all night with two restless children. I could speculate for hours about her, creating endless scenarios that would've led her to this moment. But I had no idea, nor did I know how long she had been walking that morning. Though I was curious as to why a mother of two was out at dawn, crying, and not knowing which direction she should travel, I didn't ask. I was simply concerned with her current situation. My options for finding help were few. Neither of us had a phone. I knew no one in this neighborhood, and the streets were silent. To give her directions to the mobile home park would entail many street names and turns. In her condition, it was very unlikely she was going to retain the information.

"Look," I said. "If you see a police car, wave it down. That's your best bet. I'm sure they can help." And that was all I had to offer. I felt empty. Here was a woman in a helpless situation, shuffling through town, and with no idea where to go. I pointed her in the general direction. She thanked me for stopping before we parted ways. In an hour I would be home, taking a hot shower, while she would be...well, there was no telling.

I continued my run on the trail that led around the baseball complex. The fields, dugouts, and the concessions building—so much looked as dormant as the bare trees around them. Winter was here. *Just what exactly was her story? Why the tears? How lost was she?* I could only assume her Christmas was not much to talk about. *When was the last time someone had given her a reason to smile?*

As I contemplated those questions, and rounded one of the baseball fields leading to a small parking lot, I found my own reason to smile. I came upon a police car. What were the chances?

On this quiet morning, as criminals and mischievous people were sound asleep, the cop was taking a break. I walked up as he rolled down his window.

"Excuse me, officer. I have a question."

"Well," he said, "I've got an answer. What's up?"

I told him about my encounter with the woman. I said that she appeared legit—that she wasn't putting on an act or fronting some kind of scam. She truly seemed lost and in need of assistance.

"Well then," he said. "I'll check her out."

And off he went, and off I ran, reconnecting with the trail that continued along the river again. This portion of the trail gave me an open view of the cop. I slowed my pace as I tracked his car approaching the woman and the stroller. Stopping alongside her, he rolled his passenger side window down. She leaned over and spoke while pointing in the direction I had told her to go. Moments later, he got out, walked around to her side, and opened the back door.

This is when I came to a stop. I watched him take the stroller as the mother situated the two children into the car. I thought about my iPod—about those first ten strides I had taken before making the decision to put it away. The only times I have ever returned to the car to not use my iPod has been due to threatening rain. Other than that, I continue on. And what song did I last play that stayed in my head until I met the woman?

"Watch Over You". How fitting was that?

The song, putting away the iPod that allowed me to hear the woman, the suggestion for her to wave down a cop, and then the cop. Sometimes you just have to stop and admire the unexplainable.

I had come to a "Y" in the trail. If I went right, it would take me further along the river. I chose left to go right past the cop car. And within a minute I was there. The mother was bent over, adjusting her children in the backseat. She would never see me again. Whether or not the cop had mentioned me in their discussion was insignificant. All that mattered was the last sight I caught of the cop as I ran by: a smile and a thumbs up.

Even if a day late, it's a beautiful thing witnessing the spirit of Christmas.

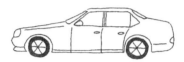

This is a car.

o True

o False

● Unsure

My Low Automotive I.Q.

If there's one place I shudder to go near, it's under the hood of a car. For therein lies the nightmare of an intimidating labyrinth of hoses, filters, valves, wires, and belts. Locating the parts that those things connect to is, for me, a complete guessing game. Though I'm proud to say I'm quite skilled at identifying the engine, the battery, and where to add the oil, I can only imagine what my moment of fame would be like in TV hell…

"Hey, Ros!! Welcome to "Find Those Things Under The Hood!!" You've got thirty minutes. Can you find the alternator? Remember… if you find it, you get the car!!!"

I'm on the show's set with the hood of a brand new Toyota Sequoia opened before me. Instead of getting busy with the task, I stand frozen, looking at the camera in front of a large studio audience. *Three million viewers!* the show's host had told me excitedly back stage, with a big, hearty pat on the shoulder. *This is your day, buddy! Own it out there. Make it happen!* My attention falls further into the camera. I'm a deer in the headlights. I'm under hypnosis. Before three million viewers, I'm a zombie staring into oblivion.

"Oh, there's no alternator in that camera," assures the host. "Might I suggest you try the car?"

I turn to the Sequoia and peer into the dizzying mechanical mess that, somewhere, contains the alternator. Truth be told, I don't even know what an alternator is. For decades I've heard the word, but I never gave it any thought. I would like to say it is a part that provides drivers alternative music through their satellite radios. I would like to say that, but I don't. *"And just why would such a music-providing device be located under the hood of a car?"* the automotive industry might ask. *"Well, that's a really, really, really good question,"* I'd say. *"Because the alternative music recording artists petitioned for it to be there?"* I do have my obvious moments of undeniable hopelessness.

With my head under the hood, and aimlessly probing at things here and there, time is running out as the host stands next to me. "It's been twenty-nine minutes, Ros. You've got sixty seconds...just where is that alternator?"

For half an hour, I've set a show record for taking the longest time to identify an automotive part. During four commercial breaks, three special guest appearances, and in front of the studio audience, confidence finally arrives. I point to the alternator seconds before the buzzer sounds. "That thing!" I say. "Yes...that thing!"

There is an awkward pause in the studio as the audience is watching a close-up of my selection on some overhead monitors. It is the pause that not only precedes disbelief, but I'm certain is widespread amongst three million viewers as well.

"That?" asks the host. *"That* is your answer?"

I have pointed to a cloudy plastic container. "Yes! *That!"*

The host's voice shifts into a consoling tone—softly sympathetic and fatherly, as if I were his son having just struck out at home plate...again. "Sorry, my friend. No alternator there. That's the car's windshield washer fluid reservoir."

It was hard to distinguish between snickers or tearful sniffles that were coming from the audience. It was also hard to locate the nearest exit sign so I could make my quick escape, and never return to that harrowing place in TV hell.

"Of course, no one walks away from here empty-handed," the host proclaims in an upbeat voice. "For playing today, you'll receive a free set of jumper cables!!"

Good grief. Where is that exit sign?

*   *   *

The labyrinth of automotive engineering beneath a vehicle's hood is highly impressive. How all of those parts fit and work in unison is beyond me. I am forever impressed by auto mechanics who diagnose and perform work on cars. Covered in grease instead of blood, and holding wrenches instead of scalpels, they are the surgeons of the automotive world.

And then there are people like me who break out in a cold sweat when we enter an auto parts store. All I need is something to make my car's interior smell better, and five steps through the front doors I'm already feeling like an idiot.

"Excuse me," I say to an employee walking by. "Do you have those tree-shaped smelly things?"

"Smelly things?"

I can feel the cold sweat beginning. Tiny ice-cold droplets beading off my forehead as if this were an arctic expedition. What am I doing here? Why didn't I just go to Hobby Lobby and buy a basket of potpourri?

"You mean an air freshener?" he says.

I roll my eyes at myself. "Yes. That's it." But I know deep down, he could've said, "You mean an alternator?" and I would've replied, "Yes. That's it."

My low automotive IQ is best illustrated (and I really hate to admit this) whenever I get an oil change. It's always some teenage boy who approaches my car and asks the world's most difficult question...

"Good morning, sir. What kind of oil would you like?"

He might as well ask me what the exact measurement of the earth's circumference is in inches. I'd probably have better luck.

I give him the easy-out answer and say, "Whatever oil you suggest."

But he's young and smart, and knows I'm an idiot, and says, "I suggest 10W-40, but would you prefer full synthetic, synthetic blend, or conventional?"

Synthetic? First thing that comes to my mind is a polyester shirt. Synthetic blend? Polyester/cotton shirt. I find myself looking at the teenager's shirt that looks very polyester, and I'm wondering if it's made out of motor oil? And why do motor oils and tax forms sound so similar? 10W-40 oil, 1040 tax form. By chance, does the IRS offer a choice between conventional and synthetic tax forms? This is all so confusing.

The teenager stands by my window, tapping his pen on a small clipboard. He seems like a nice kid, just a bit impatient. But perhaps it's because two cars have pulled in line behind me, and he simply needs an answer. My automotive IQ is not helping. As pressured and indecisive as I am, I figure out exactly what oil I want.

"I'll take a conventional synthetic high-mileage 10W-40 Schedule B please."

His pen stops tapping, just falls dead. He's not writing down a single thing I've said. I'm the worst. The absolute worst possible customer. And I'm a grown man. How did I ever make it this far in life without knowing what oil to get, how to articulate a tree-shaped air-freshener, or possess any knowledge of the alternator? A third car has now pulled in line behind me.

"Sir, a 'schedule B'? That kind of oil doesn't exist."

I shouldn't exist. Not in this line anyway. I can't even give an educated guess regarding what type of oil my car needs. And my poor car. To think I am its owner. If there were ever a Car Protective Services agency, I'd be on their radar.

The kid's pen resumes tapping. A cold sweat runs down my temples. I need out of here.

"Excuse me," I say, as I put the car in drive. "I forgot to feed my fish." And drive away.

Feed my fish? That's the best I could come up with??? A quarter mile down the street, I get the feeling that I need to redeem myself, to make things right, or at least prove that I'm not a complete automotive flop.

Then I see it. I hit the brakes and make a sharp right turn. A big smile forms instantly as I come to a stop. I roll down my window to be greeted by an attendant. "Good morning, sir! Welcome to The Car Wash. What can we do for you today?"

My smile grows larger. I'm in heaven. This is my car, and I know my car. "The Works," I say. "I'll take The Works."

"Great choice," he says. "Nothing better than someone who knows what he needs."

I step out of the car, hand him the keys, then walk off into the sunshine toward the waiting room. It is the start of a very good day.

Bucket

It happened during halftime at a Texas State men's basketball game when a man entered the arena with a dog. The Yellow Labrador Retriever led him down a flight of steps, sniffing right and left as he went. Occasionally, the man stopped to shake hands with acquaintances while his companion obediently waited by his side. "C'mon, Bucket," he said to the dog. "This way." As they descended the steps, students lifted their heads up from their cell phones. Word quickly and excitedly spread, "Look! Look at the dog!" Within this shift of interest—from phones to a dog—it dawned on me that no matter how advanced technology becomes, it can't compete with the animal kingdom (or nature for that matter) in capturing our attention and making lasting memories.

No dog tricks were required to notice Bucket. No jumping through hoops, laser light show, or walking on hind legs were needed for his introduction. Rather, it was simply the slow and methodical meandering of four soft paws that had us all curiously drawn to the dog's purpose. Why was Bucket here? Tap the man on the shoulder, ask a few questions, and before you know it, word has spread that Bucket is a 2-year-old K9 detection working dog who has been trained to identify 16 scents used in making explosive devices. But as impressive as his background is, that's not what intrigued us at first sight. What excited us and made us smile was his mere presence.

In a similar setting, I once attended a San Antonio Spurs basketball game when a bat entered the arena. Its seemingly erratic flight sent it all over the court, often coming close to the players. Of course, the bat displayed no obedient personality, but everyone was fascinated, and quickly caring less about the game itself. The bat's unpredictable movements kept us inquisitively engaged.

*   *   *

We all know the feeling of acquiring something brand new like a car, TV, cell phone, or a computer. That initial infatuation—so clean, unscathed, and seemingly perfect within their flawless designs. We handle them with utmost care, like rare artifacts that will fall to ruin if we don't. But time passes quickly, and soon we get so accustomed to their function that they become nothing more than objects of service.

In a world that expects advances in technology, there is no going back to earlier versions of computation, graphic display or engineering. Either you continue to build faster, sleeker products or you pay the price for not having met people's expectations.

And then there is the constant of nature that requires no innovation to attract our attention. We are forever intrigued. Wasps building their nests the same way they always have. The Monarch butterfly migration repeats itself century after century. A field of golden Nebraska wheat swaying in the breeze. The heavy grumble of thunder following a lightning strike. A dog named Bucket. Nature plugs along at the same pace it always has, and yet it is what truly enthralls us. In a world that demands innovations and technological advances, given the choice, it is the unchanging world of nature that holds our memories best.

*   *   *

A man drives his brand new, fully-loaded, 2-door black Acura through the streets of a Colorado mountain town. The car is nimble, handling perfectly. The sound system punctuates the machine's interior with a bass that powerfully thumps as if the man were inside the artist's recording studio. He runs his hand over the leather upholstery, totally in awe of the car's craftsmanship. Everything is simply too good to be true.

But then, he sees a cluster of brake lights ahead of him, and all traffic comes to a stop. He turns the music down, and looks ahead to figure out what the issue is. There are no police cars or fire trucks. No signs that a fresh accident might have occurred. Not even a stranded motorist with a flat tire.

Then he sees it, and it all makes sense. As if out for an afternoon stroll, an elk takes its time crossing four lanes of traffic. It even stops to face the front row of cars, as if contemplating whether or not to walk across their hoods. People are taking pictures, pointing through their windshields. Several get out to find a clearer view. But everyone's fascination is doubled as the elk begins walking between the rows of cars, as if it were conducting a security checkpoint inspection. The man in the Acura watches intently as the elk passes by his window. Seven hundred pounds of Rocky Mountain wildlife drifts by in nonchalant fashion, and then exits the street to disappear into the woods, leaving behind a grateful audience.

We are completely content with the constant of nature. It exists and excites us within its original version. There are no bells or whistles needed to improve it.

As the years roll by, the man's experience will forever be remembered and passed on....

"So, we're all stopped in this big traffic jam, and I have no idea what's going on. I had bought a new car that day. It was an Acura. Anyway, I then see this big elk, just taking his time like there was no tomorrow. He stops and looks at us. And we're all looking at him. And it's like you could tell we didn't want him to leave. He then starts walking around the cars, and right by my window. I almost reached out to touch him. He was that much of a gift. I'll never forget it."

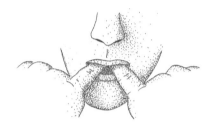

The Drool King

Who are these people who can so easily put their fingers in their mouths and send out a loud and high-pitched whistle? It leaves you wondering if it's more of a trick than them actually doing it.

The other day, Jane, a 78-year-old friend of mine, stood next to me as I attempted to get someone's attention in the distance. Not exactly knowing what I was doing, I shoved my two pinkies deep into the sides of my mouth. I'd seen people finger-whistle many times before, and I felt like I was doing what would create the right sound. Unfortunately, instead of a seasoned whistler, I think I looked more like a fish caught on two lures. But that wasn't nearly as bad as the sound I created—like the muffled hiss of an angry raccoon. And though hissing raccoons don't drool, this one did. Like a Saint Bernard, I drooled down my chin only to make the mistake of quickly whipping my head away from Jane, which only guaranteed slobber slinging across my face.

I get frustrated when I fail at something that seems so simple… like the skateboard. It's a piece of wood on four little wheels, four inches off the street. What could possibly go wrong at four inches? My tailbone, wrists, elbows, knees, hips, chest, and back is what. I'd probably make a full-body lift-off into the air like I had been ejected from a race car. And then there are the jugglers—those kids in the park who talk to you about whatever it is you want to talk about as they juggle four, five, or six tennis balls. Could there not be a more deceptive skill than juggling? Two tennis balls, and I can juggle with the best of them. Add one more and I'm fumbling around in all directions like I'm dodging a swarm of bees. I know, I know…these things that people do…they just make it look so easy. They're not world-class athletes. They're just average Joes and Janes. And that's the thing that kills me…if they're average, then what am I?

As my daughter, Bailey, would often remind me throughout her sarcastic childhood…I'm a loser.

Certainly I'd conquer the whistle on my second attempt. I put my pinkies back in my mouth, but this time not so far that it looked as if I were probing for my tonsils. I set them in half-way, then blew out the same repulsive sound while spilling more spittle down my chin, understandably causing Jane to shudder and squirm. I mean, I was an analogous disaster at work: part fish, part raccoon, and part dog—a hybrid mess gone wrong in the animal kingdom.

"Is this what you're trying to do?" says Jane, putting her two index fingers in her mouth. Jane sends out a whistle that pierces my ears with a sharp delivery. I'm awed by how easy she makes it look. How many years had it taken her to perfect this penetrating shrill? The person, whose attention I had been trying to get, turns immediately. I wave to him, and he waves back. Just a friendly hello was all I was after, as I take full credit for the whistle.

"Really?" says Jane.

"Really," I say. "Now watch this…"

I put my index fingers in my mouth so they're positioned in a "V" with just a small space between the finger tips. *IT WAS THE INDEX FINGERS!!…NOT THE PINKIES!!…HOW EASY IS THIS!!!???* I am doing *exactly* as Jane did.

One deep inhalation, and then I blow air forcefully through the gap. Such power. Such precision. Such slobber stringing over my lips. I'm a disaster. Even the raccoon hiss is gone. It sounds more like a suction device during a dental procedure.

"That's pretty bad," Jane says chuckling. "Prehhh-ty bad."

I look at Jane and her god-awful righteous smile. I want to say "to hell with it," and push this near-80-year-old woman off her feet. I want to tie her to a skateboard and send her speeding down a hill. And though admittedly ill-behaved, before I do that, I want to spit on her feet and tell her, "Farewell!"

But I can't. There's a bit of a problem…I'm out of saliva.

The Last Day

Ican only hope that my final moments in this life will be spent living instead of dying. By that I'm referring to my mental state, not my physical. Of course I'd like to have the best of both worlds, but given the choice, I want to be aware—to be cognizant of my surroundings. Even if I'm destined to be confined to a hospital bed, I want to be able to ask the nurse to please turn the light off as she leaves. I want her to know that what I said wasn't a metaphor to be interpreted as her playing the part of Death, encroaching to forever turn off *my* light. As I acknowledge the dispelled notion of such a metaphor, I hope that she will respond with a chuckle. Because, after all, is there really any better way to enter darkness than immediately after making someone smile?

But what if you are dying? What if your sickness is getting the best of you? In a previous story I mentioned my Uncle Ike who had lived a very full life immersed in the medical fields at Duke and Vanderbilt universities. His last day of life was not comfortable, as he had been experiencing a considerable amount of pain. My mother was in his bedroom that night when he asked her, "What is today's date?" She told him, then asked why he wanted to know that. He said, "Just want to know the date I'm going to die." Here he was, the scientist in his final hours of life, and wanting to collect the facts before he took his last breath. Information that he would never retrieve, but important information to him at the time, because he was *alive*, not dying.

He needed the medical attention that only a hospital could provide. When the paramedics arrived, he was strapped onto a gurney to be loaded into an ambulance. He knew there wasn't going to be enough oxygen to make it to the hospital on time. This was it—he was going to arrive unconscious. His final words to his family were: "Be sure to shut down the oxygen tanks…you don't want to have the house blow up while you're gone." He was now the scientist, the man watching out for others, the man coherently thinking in the right direction, and the man who would never relinquish his unrelenting style of dry humor. He was just engaged in, and keenly aware of, his surroundings.

Again, he was *alive*.

I am not a scientist. My lifeblood flows with creative juices. While I see the facts of life, I have a tendency to dwell on the what-ifs of impossible wonders. My mind travels to many places obscure, and somehow, within the obscurity, I find normalcy. My Uncle Ike, however, would comically just roll his eyes and, in effect, say to my mother: "Lucy, this child of yours—he was certainly born half-baked."

So, if I may be so lucky to have all of my faculties together, I wonder what my last thought will be before I die. Will I be so lucky to engage in something creative? Perhaps an interesting perspective will strike me to such an extent that it will later be recalled that… "He left us with the quintessential Ros."

Go ahead, sheath me in discomfort and confine me to a hospital bed. But at least give me a window so I can gaze at that portion of the world. Maybe I'll see a young bird attempting to fly, and that will remind me of the Wright brothers, who will remind me that creativity and science can be beautiful partners. And the word science will remind me of Uncle Ike, and I'll suddenly realize that I'm in the exact point in life where he learned of the date that he died. I'll smile, because, like my uncle, I'll be in a place of full clarity. And what better way to enter darkness than immediately after a smile.

"Nurse, I'm going to get some sleep now. Please turn off my light."

Common Ground

Ilooked straight into the eye of an elk today. He was grazing on some tall grass just thirty feet down a slope from where I stood. That big, dark, glassy eye stayed on me like a great conversation. Never blinking and fully engaged. It's always been about the eyes. They tell so much, and how quickly they connect.

I had been creeping up on him in the woods for a closer look. Thick, matted clumps of dark brown fur dangled from his throat. His mid-section was embedded with what appeared to be abrasions where the fur had been rutted from some sort of encounter. A predator? The hard strike of another bull's antlers during a fight? Or he might have been entangled in a cluster of stubborn tree branches. It was hard to say.

As he tugged and chewed on the grass, I slowly positioned myself behind the one pine tree that stood between us. Perhaps I had come too close. My curiosity had completely ignored the possibility that this elk might charge me if his instincts deemed necessary. He lifted his head at my movement, so that two eyes instead of one were now fixated on me. His thick, wooly neck stretched tall and unbending like a soldier at attention. He was on high alert, studying me. The ten points of his antlers, if I were caught in the open, would slice and gouge me to an inevitable death. The sharp, explosive kicks of his hooves would crack my bones and sever my tendons, disabling any attempt for me to crawl and claw myself back to life.

But we continued to stare at each other—neither of us moving. I wasn't sure what to anticipate. I wasn't sure what to do. I only knew that his mass was at least four times that of mine. What was the purpose of me coming this close? Why couldn't my curiosity have been satisfied to stay a hundred yards back? His eyes, however—there was something going on. Perhaps we were each seeing the same thing.

And perhaps that is why he then relaxed. This soldier stood at ease. As if some part of his instincts had told him I was as harmless as the pine tree or the breeze that swept through it. As if our eyes had discovered a mutual understanding that this was common ground. Could it be that he did not run, because he trusted me? Could it be that I did not flee either, because I trusted him? I would like to say, yes. I would like to believe that something wonderful did, in fact, occur. Perhaps indescribable, but, still, wonderful. Because of an elk, I was fully alive.

For fifteen minutes I watched him feed on the tall grass, shifting his weight in the pine needles and sandy ground as he ate. For fifteen minutes I admired his presence with all that I could, because I knew that the moment of our final separation was approaching. The grass was sparse here. He would have to move further into the woods to appease his appetite. For fifteen minutes I watched him, until he disappeared.

Funeral of the Seas

Thanks to the movie *The Big Lebowski*, I never want to be cremated. I am convinced I would have equal or worse luck...

Steve Buscemi plays "Donny", whose ashes are put in a coffee can. John Goodman (Walter) and Jeff Bridges (The Dude) take Donny to a cliff overlooking the Pacific Ocean where they plan to scatter his remains. After Walter delivers as bad of a eulogy as you could ask for, he takes off the coffee can lid. It's poor timing as a gust of wind blows Donny's ashes away from the ocean and straight into The Dude's bearded face.

I could only hope that I might end up in a coffee can. But, no, fate would steer the two warped minds of those handling me in another direction...

"I got an empty container of motor oil we could put him in."

"Naw. Too difficult. How 'bout a jar of spaghetti sauce I finished last night?"

"Hell, if we wanna make things really easy, then let's go with a paper sack."

"Genius! That's it! A paper sack!"

And off I'd go, stuffed in a paper sack in the back seat of a car—lodged between a bag of dog food and a package of toilet paper.

"Where d'you wanna dump him?"

"I dunno. Where d'you wanna dump him?"

"Well, he did mention the Gulf of Mexico. He always talked 'bout the ocean."

"Uh, that's like three hours away. Ain't driving no paper sack for three hours."

"But ya would dog food an' toilet paper?"

"Absolutely. They're necessities."

Of course, any chance of my making it even remotely close to the ocean would be slim due to the presence of a third occupant in the car: a black Labrador Retriever named Sniff. While my buddies are in the front, continuing their intellectual conversation fit for an audience of morons, Sniff is in back and getting mighty curious about my body bag. He's not hungry, so the dog food doesn't interest him, and neither does the pine-scented toilet paper. But the paper sack...now that's something to investigate! In no time, he burrows his wet muzzle so deep inside that his nostrils get annoyingly clogged with ashes. Igniting into a psychotic growling fit, he makes the mistake of raising his head to shake the sack free. All of my remains—all that I ever was—come pouring out like an open bag of flour. As the car comes to a screeching halt, Sniff cannons three sneezes. Sneeze #1 propels the sack off of his head. Sneeze #2 fires tiny, moist, snotty ash clods into the rear window that stick like spit wads. And sneeze #3 launches additional clods directly behind the neck of the driver.

"Damnit, Sniff!!" he hollers, looking into the rear view mirror. "Good Lord! All over the toilet paper! Look at you—all covered with death!"

And that's as close as I'd get to the ocean. The majority of me sharing space with fleas in Sniff's fur.

"Throw it out!"

"The dog?"

"No, you idiot. The sack...throw it out!"

"Seriously? Isn't that kinda disrespectful?"

"What's there to respect? There's ashes all over Sniff and my car!"

"But what about the ocean? He wanted to end up in the deep blue sea."

"SCREW THE OCEAN!! THROW THE DAMN SACK OUT!! HE CAN ENJOY THE DEEP BLACK ASPHALT!!"

I'm telling you...if I'm ever to be cremated, I guarantee that's as good as it'll ever get. But if I do want to end up in the ocean, then how will I ever get there?

I have an idea. Write a letter.

*   *   *

Dear Royal Caribbean Cruise Lines:

Imagine firing multitudes of deceased bodies from a cannon off the rear deck of one of your ships, and making bookoos of money doing so. Enticing, isn't it!? You may not realize this, but if Royal Caribbean runs with my idea, then it will be at the helm of innovation. It's time for a better way to pass into the afterlife than we are currently accustomed to. It's time for a cruise ship named...*Funeral of the Seas*.

Let me explain...

Funerals aren't cheap. We dish out thousands of dollars in order to make the dead comfortable (or so we're led to believe). A fully velvet-lined, solid mahogany or stainless steel casket complete with a cozy, over-sized pillow is sold under the guise that without luxurious bedding, our loved ones will experience nothing but eternal bed sores. The casket has only a few hours of viewing time before it's forever lowered into the earth to share the dirt with grubs, beetles, worms, ants, and centipedes. Such a beautiful piece of craftsmanship, but never to be seen again (unless a careless city utility worker accidentally digs up a sewer pipe while texting his girlfriend). Whatever happened to burying bodies and nothing more? It was a custom that worked fine for thousands of years. Bury Uncle Joe, then let the good earth absorb and recycle him. And best of all, Uncle Joe's death didn't cost but a few nickels.

If we're going to spend thousands of dollars on our loved one's funerals, then let's make it a *few* thousand, not several thousand. And let's send them away in a style yet to be experienced in the funeral industry. I'm talking about a massive potato gun. Confused? Oh, not to worry! Let me continue...

I shall use myself as an example. One day I die. Then what?

All to be explained in another conversation, but because I'm convinced that a black lab named Sniff will completely blow any chance of my being cremated with a peaceful and beautiful exit from this life, my only option is a burial, which, as you've gathered, I'm not much in favor of either.

Instead of being buried, I want to be released. I want to take a lifeless swan dive off the rear deck of *Funeral of the Seas*. It may not be the most graceful swan dive, as I'm sure my entry into the water might be a disastrous belly flop, a harrowing back slap, or even a sloppy face plant — all complete with flailing limbs. And just how would I dive from a cruise ship? I would do it not with the parting push from a couple of friends or loved ones, but rather with the soon-to-be patented Corpse Cannon. Basically, as previously mentioned, it's a larger scale potato gun that generates pneumatic pressure created by compressed gas, and can fire a human body over 500 feet. I mean, seriously, what better way to go!? Sailing into the ocean air with no inhibitions, no errand lists, no car payments, and no more commercials—Heaven.

Of course, once I hit the water, understand there'll be no need for friends and loved ones to have to witness any type of cruel carnivorous feeding, as I'll have been thoroughly coated with the soon-to-be patented 3M SharkAway Repellant, and sporting my 40-pound weighted strength training vest. As *Funeral of the Seas* cruises off into the sunset, how fitting all of this would be as I submerge in the ship's wake.

Total cost for a cruise ship funeral: $3,000. It'd be an out-and-back one-day trip. Details of large walk-in freezers to store the dearly departed can all be worked out. All Royal Caribbean has to do is schmooze with the rules and regulations departments that oversee the operations of funeral businesses, play a few rounds of golf with the higher-ups, and there won't be any difficulty getting approval for the soon-to-be and highly sought after Corpse Cannon funerals.

That's all I have for now. Please feel free to contact me anytime. Now, if you'll excuse me, I need to have a little alone time to deal with the aforementioned dog named Sniff who's living rent-free in my head.

Bon voyage,
Ros Hill

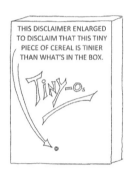

A Matter of Taste

I need to say a few words to the breakfast cereal companies of this country…

Part of me wants to take a baseball bat to your knees, drag you helplessly into a bowl of spoiled milk, and then watch you drown in soggy misery—all for insulting my intelligence.

But since that might come across as a bit harsh, perhaps I'll just settle for asking you one question: *Really?*

I mean, really…must your cereal boxes inform me that the cereal in the photograph has been "Enlarged to show texture"? Do you think I'm going to file some sort of class-action lawsuit for false representation of the true-to-life smaller size cereal inside the box? And why print the disclaimer with a font whose letters are no bigger than dust mites? If you want to say it, then say it…"ATTENTION CONSUMERS!!! THE CEREAL FLAKES IN THIS PHOTOGRAPH ARE FIFTY TIMES THEIR ORIGINAL SIZE. OUR ONLY INTENTION IS TO SHOW TEXTURE. WE DEBATED MAKING IT LARGER, BUT THAT WOULD'VE MADE THE FLAKES LOOK LIKE COW PATTIES… AND ANYTHING RESEMBLING DRIED POOP WOULD CERTAINLY GET US IN DEEP DOO-DOO."

If they're not showing texture, then it's "detail." And if neither of those suits their liking, then companies like organic-conscious Kashi have taken their disclaimer not just a step further, but in an obscure direction. In fact, it's hard to discern whether they're serious about their word choice or are just flat out playing with us…

*   *   *

Extremely hungry, I was shoveling in spoonfuls of Kashi's Cinnamon Harvest. I repeatedly plunged my spoon into my bowl at such a voracious pace, I nearly bypassed the chewing phase and went straight to swallowing. Slurping the milk. Smacking my lips. I can eat with the best of toddlers. And then, staring at the cereal box, I saw it: Kashi's disclaimer… "Enlarged to show taste."

Taste?

Since when can you *see* taste? That's like biting into an apple and saying, "Boy, this sounds red." Just doesn't make sense. I truly appreciate Kashi's attempt to wrap my brain around the unthinkable, but entering any kind of fourth dimensional thinking goes way beyond the simplicity I prefer when looking at a cereal box. When I try to comprehend a picture showing taste, all I can manage is a monstrous migraine headache. Multiply my pain and suffering times…let's say… one million people who eat Kashi cereals, and you're not only looking at pharmacies that can't keep up with the demand for headache drugs, but a class-action lawsuit demanding justice served through compensation. Personally, I don't think Kashi's disclaimer has a prayer in a court of law.

But Kashi is not the company I'd have my crosshairs on. It'd be Kellogg's. That's right, the mother of all breakfast cereal companies. I, of course, would elect to represent myself. After all, I know cereal. It's been *the* staple food for my entire life. At any time of the day, I can engulf a bowl of cereal like taking in a nice breath of fresh air. Move aside you unqualified attorneys…I got this!…

Supreme Court of the United States
Ros Hill v. Kellogg's
(*Official transcript*)
Elena Kagan, Associate Justice, presiding

Justice Kagan: "Mr. Hill, you are representing yourself in the case, is this not true?"

Me: "Trick question, your Honor?"

JK: "Mr. Hill do you know where you are?"

Me: "Thirty feet from you? Thirty-five? Your Honor, I'm not trying to be funny, but just answering the question. I could've said third rock from the sun and that, too, would've been a correct answer."

JK: "Mr. Hill, it's now going on thirty seconds into this hearing, and you already have two strikes against you. One more strike and I shall have you escorted out for contempt of court. Am I being clear, Mr. Hill?"

Me: "Yes, ma'am—I mean, your Honor! Sorry, sorry, sorry! Please don't strike me on that one. An honest mistake, your Honor."

JK: "Let us begin…Mr. Hill, I see that you are suing the Kellogg's Corporation for the amount of $329 million for 'befuddlelingly fraudulent advertising' showing taste. *Befuddlelingly?* Is that even a word? Mr. Hill, I must ask you…Is this a typo in what I'm reading? Just how can you show taste? And how did you ever come up with that highly exorbitant amount?"

Me: "Good questions, your Honor. $329 million is derived from my birthday…March 29. I figure if you're gonna get a gift, then make it a birthday gift! Moving on…Kellogg's has a subsidiary company called Kashi, and on the front of the box of Cinnamon Harvest it states: 'Enlarged to show taste.' And I'm like, enlarged to show taste? Like what the F? I mean, like really? Your Honor, I sense we're on the same page here. Quite a *befuddlelingly* mess, isn't it?"

JK: "Mr. Hill, I need to say something. And I'll be blunt. Just how the hell did this case make it to the Supreme Court?"

Me: "Your Honor, I'll be happy to answer that, but first I must ask one thing: are you allowed to say 'hell' in court? Cuz I almost dropped the F bomb a minute ago. And I'm thinkin', if you can say hell, then I can maybe get away with f—."

The last thing I remember was Justice Kagan putting three fingers in the air, just before some burly Marine-like dude put me in a choke hold and dragged me out of the room. I wasn't sure if the applause was for my great oratory or my strike-out at home plate. I can only presume the former.

Miraculously, justice did prevail. Well, sort of.

Though Justice Kagan denied my request of monetary compensation, she did acknowledge and reward my pain and suffering in her Opinion:

"It is with a strange unfolding of my opinion regarding Ros Hill v. Kellogg's that I have found an unfortunate understanding for a need to compensate Mr. Hill. I say unfortunate, because I plain just don't like the guy. However, Justice never favors on the merits of likes or dislikes of personality. Mr. Hill not-so-eloquently stated that 'a million other poor souls whose minds are bent and harmed from trying to figure out Kashi's fourth dimensional brain-fart, taste-enigma' should receive equal distribution for the amount of $329 million. I have denied that request. However, as difficult as this is for me to say, I must agree that Kashi's taste disclaimer is…god forgive me here…befuddlelingly bizarre. It is with sound mind that I do hereby order Kellogg's to compensate Mr. Hill's mental anguish with 329 boxes of Cinnamon Harvest, all to have the exclusive disclaimer that will say: 'Enlarged because it is.' Happy Birthday, Mr. Hill. This case is over!"

The Zipper

S ome people are indifferent about bugs. They don't love them. They don't hate them. Bugs are bugs. *Oh, look...it's a cricket on my shoulder! What an amazing little creature!*

Not me.

A cricket lands on my shoulder, and I don't even give it a chance to be identified. As I slap whatever it is far into the yard, I shudder and squirm while making a pitiful, crybaby-like face as if I just witnessed someone slowly chewing a mouthful of live worms.

I go through the same physical gyrations whenever I see a spider larger than a dime. Especially if it's within six inches of my face and closing fast, such as the time I was cursed with rotten luck while riding my lawn mower.

I had been cutting the grass for about an hour—eyes down, focused on the pathway—when, by chance, I happened to look up, and spotted a zipper spider, known for the zipper-like design spun in the center of their webs. They are black and yellow, and make Death look more approachable. Websites will tell you zipper spiders can get up to 1.5 inches long. This is a lie. Their bodies alone are the size and volatility of a hand grenade, and legs like knitting needles. Other unreliable sources will tell you the spiders are basically harmless, that they only deliver a bee-like sting. Another lie. Zipper spiders can devour goats, flocks of birds, and human heads in an hour. It is my personal belief that they can also hurl large stones over fifty feet. It's not a matter of whether or not you can escape their super glue-like webs, but rather how fast you can run.

I was all white knuckles on the mower as panic coursed through my brain. I took my foot off the accelerator, then began madly stomping the metal floor board where a small brake pedal was located...somewhere. How many thousands of times had I stepped on that brake pedal without looking? And now, as I coasted closer to the spider, my size 13 shoe was failing me.

Six inches from nose-planting into *arachnida vampirea*, my foot finally found the brake pedal. I hit it hard, but that might not have been the best decision as the sudden change in direction lurched me forward...

*   *   *

Maybe this isn't a story about my fear of spiders. Maybe it was never intended to be all about me. Maybe it's about understanding and acceptance. Maybe that's a stretch?

I don't think so.

One more inch, and I would've touched the web. It would've been my end. The zipper spider would've consumed my head within the hour. But there was no chance as the miracle of the mower's reverse pedal backed me safely away.

Twenty feet out, I stopped and shut off the engine. My heart pounding, I needed to cut the grass beneath the web and beyond. I had only one option...destroy the spider.

I went into the house and snatched a broom from the pantry. It's always been my go-to weapon of destruction when dealing with domestic critters. I've shot many scorpions across the kitchen floor like they were hockey pucks. And spiders...oh, I've cleared countless pathways blocked by their annoying webs.

The spider hadn't budged. It was positioned directly over its zipper webbing. Even standing six feet away, I felt extremely vulnerable. Ok, I might have exaggerated a little. So it didn't eat goats or flocks of birds. So it really was about 1.5 inches in length. So what. It still had the ability to mess with my mind.

I turned with my left side facing the spider, then took a batter's stance, holding the broom like a bat. Eye on the target. One mighty swing and I'd smash it out of the yard. But then came the memory of my Little League baseball coach from decades ago. He was always reminding me of the basic fundamental tenets of the game. "Don't just swing at any pitch," he'd say. "Make sure it's the *right* pitch." How many times had I swung at pitches too high or too low and, in the process, struck out? How many times had I walked back to the dugout feeling dejected because I knew I had made a poor decision? Too many.

The zipper spider's web—what an incredible architectural construction of innate ability. Despite how much I detest spiders, I could not deny its impressive geometrical design. The spider's survival was dependent upon the strength and placement of its web, which had been spun between a vegetable garden's fence post and a bush. Outside of violent weather and brush fires, the web's integrity was vulnerable to one major threat: man.

Knees bent and feet slightly more than shoulder width apart, I settled into an athletic position. To generate the most power, I shifted my weight to the back leg. Like golf, the most effective swing comes from a relaxed grip, but the mere presence of the spider forced my hands to choke the broom.

Make sure it's the right pitch.

What could possibly be wrong with this pitch? I hated spiders, and this particular one was right in the strike zone. But in the moment of giving myself the green light to swing, I was interrupted by a moth that had carelessly flown into the web, and with no hope of escaping. There it would perish, destined to be a meal for one.

Sure enough, I watched the spider quickly react to the vibrations of its web, before spreading its legs over the moth and silencing it.

I found myself not favoring the spider's predatory mastery, nor seeking to interfere and save the moth (how I would have accomplished that, I have no idea). I relaxed my grip on the broom and brought it down to my side. Watching and accepting the scene as a whole, I let the spider be. Even though my annihilation of the spider could have been defined as "natural" since I am part of nature, I chose to isolate myself from such destruction, and admire the mechanical engineering required to stabilize the web. I was embarking on an understanding of just how mathematical spiders are. Their instinctive knowledge of trigonometry in relation to angular tensions is unmatched within the animal kingdom. As much as I hated this spider, I decided not to swat it to smithereens, but basically gave it freedom to move about my yard. For a moment—well, several moments—I wondered if I had simply lost my mind.

*   *   *

Some people are indifferent about bugs. They don't love them. They don't hate them. Bugs are bugs. *Oh, look...it's a cricket on my shoulder! What an amazing little creature!*

Yep, that's me.

Socks

The man walked inside my exhibit tent, wearing an old T-shirt, tattered cargo shorts, running shoes, and a pair of mismatched socks. He was about 30 years old, average build, and quiet. I said, "Good morning" to him and a few others who began congregating in the booth. Everyone responded appropriately, except for the man with the mismatched socks who stood close to one of my paintings, craning his neck and squinting his eyes as if undergoing an inspection. I couldn't help but study his mismatched socks that had peculiar designs. From where I stood it was hard to make them out, so I sat down in my chair and discreetly leaned forward to get a better look. We were now two men simultaneously inspecting each other's property—one possibly intrigued by the sweet fruits of creativity or just killing time, the other by socks.

Bicycles. Each sock had a different bicycle design repeated on them. The athlete in me looked at his calves. They were developed, like they had endured plenty of pedaling. Having a past of eating up the miles racing road bikes, I asked him, "Excuse me, but road or trail?"

He looked down at his socks, "Road," he said. "All road."

"Do you race?" I asked.

"Hardly. I ride to work," he said. He then returned to his quiet self that I took as being rather uninviting.

Behind him was a small table displaying my children's books. A middle-aged woman stood nearby. "Would you sign one to my mother? She collects books like these."

"Of course," I said. "I'd be happy to." I personalized her book, and took care of a couple of print sales as well.

After everyone had left, the man turned his attention to the books, then walked over and began flipping through the pages of *Unexpected Tails*. "Your work is really clever," he said. "It's very *New Yorker...* cerebral. These situations in which you depict wildlife—unusual, yet conveyed so well. And the humor...I just love the humor."

His demeanor seemed average, like the type of person at a party whom I might avoid because I knew there wasn't going to be much to talk about. But this man suddenly lit a spark. His word selection and literary reference just didn't seem to match who I thought I was talking to. *Yet who was I talking to? Who had I made him to be?* Not *that* educated was perhaps my first thought. But there was so much more to come. This man was not only about to open my eyes, and lead me down a path unfolding some telltale signs of his life that were...well...may I say, indicatively beautiful.

I was curious about his biking as well as intellect. Funny how quickly the tables turn. One moment you've passed him as an average Joe, and the next you don't want Joe to leave.

"So, you bike to work," I said. "Is that difficult in San Antonio? I mean so many cars."

"Not at all. I take a scenic route. No better way to travel."

"And good exercise," I said.

"Oh, so much more than that. I'm not encased in a car. I'm outside and listening to all the birds. Nothing like the sound of birds in the morning."

I would have been completely content had this been the only person I'd encountered at the show. I could never have made a single sale, and I would've gone home a far wealthier man than when I began that day. Not a dime in my pocket to show for a single sale, yet my pocket would be stuffed. This man was an observer who saw the pieces of the whole. And it was the want of his curiosity that not only fulfilled him, but had drawn me in as his audience of one.

So we talked about birds. He said he found it interesting how such a foreign language intrigues us. "We have general ideas about their communication, but we don't know if they speak with inflection." Now he had my mind going... *Is there something going on between the chirps, like nuances of expression? Is there dialogue? Are there two birds out there arguing over who did a half-ass job constructing the nest?* Riding his bike into a cool breeze on his way to work was one thing. Add an endless series of musical trees along his way, and it was all he could ask for.

"So, where do you ride to?" I asked. "Where do you work?"

"The zoo."

"And what do you do there?"

Without hesitation, he smiled and said, "I clean up after the animals. I clean up their poop."

"That's your job? Like that's what you do?"

"Pretty much."

I wasn't getting the full story. And I wasn't about to let his intellectual insight and mismatched socks just walk away from me to remember him as that guy who swept up poop. I knew I was two questions away from tapping into what really made him tick. It's not easy getting personal with someone you've only known for ten minutes, but...what the hell...

"Okay," I said. "I have to admit, you have me very intrigued. You're smart, you're educated, and you see the world in a way that most people don't. You're not just an observer, but rather someone who dives into what he's seeing. You get *into* it. But this zoo job of yours...I mean that's what you do...I get that...but why? I mean what about ambition?"

For the first time, there was a pause in his answer. He lightly bounced his head as if conceding, *Okay, you win.*

"The job—it's all about my mother," he said. "She's ill, and can't really take care of herself. So I looked for a job that was easy, outside, and close by with flexible hours. No, it's not a dream job, but it works. I'm able to give her a lot of attention."

As if that wasn't enough for me to praise the guy, he then went on to address my second question...

"Ambition? I'm pretty familiar with it. I have a double-degree from Boston University in psychology and biology. I plan to move up as a specialist animal caretaker. This current job is just a stepping stone. It generates just enough money to keep me afloat for tending to mom."

He looked at one of my framed originals titled, *Fear Of Heights,* which depicts a lioness sheepishly looking upwards as she walks through the legs of a large group of giraffes.

"You know," he said, "There's so much behavior in animals. And so I share a lot of my knowledge with the people visiting the zoo. I see the caretakers in their uniforms, but I don't see them engaging with the public and educating them, like going out of their way to talk to the folks. You can only imagine what I must look like, walking up to them with a poop collector in one hand, a broom in the other, and then telling them about ostrich mating habits. Understandably, they're not quite sure what to make of me, but I think that all quickly fades as they can tell I know my shit."

We both laughed as he concluded, "Well, you know."

Soon after that, our conversation ended. He purchased a few note cards, then we shook hands as I wished him well. I told him I'd try to make a trip to the zoo so that he could give me his inside animal information tour.

And who knows, if I leave early enough, I just might find him on his bike commuting to work. He certainly will be easy to spot—the man smiling as he pedals, and listening to the music in the trees.

A Nugget of Wisdom

I was exhibiting my art at the Pecan Street Art Festival in Austin, Texas, when a boy about seven years old and his parents walked up to my booth. I always do a signing for my children's books which I set on a table at the entrance. The boy was enthralled with the books—his eyes grew larger each time he turned a page. "Mom! Dad! Come see these!"

What could be more beautiful than the excited voice of a child calling his parents to join him in a moment of discovery? What could possibly deter the parents from giving him their attention? Perhaps a round of bickering between the mother and father...

"We should go," he said. "It's too hot anyway."

"But we just got here." she replied.

"I don't like the heat."

"It's not too hot."

"There are too many people anyway."

She looked him straight in the eyes. "This is ridiculous. Why'd we even come?"

He shot a stare directly back at her and said, "That's what I'm sayin'."

As they stood a few feet behind their son, the father ordered, "Put down the book. We need to keep moving."

Continuing to flip through the pages, the child was captivated by the book. "Look at this whale!"

The dad elevated his voice. "Let's go!"

Shaking her head, the mother said, "Just great. So glad we came today."

The father grabbed his son's arm, and led him away. That was the last time I would ever see them.

Just a parental dispute? Not quite. There was more to it that caught my eye.

It was the father. I could not stop looking at him. And in doing so, I could not stop thinking about the boy. What were his chances of growing up without being bombarded by negative influences? In fact, I had wondered about that before the three had arrived at my booth. In the distance I had spotted the father wearing a tank top. On the front of it, and in large bold letters, it read:

**SHUT
THE
F**K
UP!**

I get it. Blatant. In-your-face shock value. A rebellious streak has been riding on your shoulders for quite some time, years in fact. Say what you want and express it as you wish. But, dude, you're about 35 years of age, and you have a young, impressionable boy. I don't care if you're walking the streets at a crowded art fair or grilling burgers in the backyard…trash the shirt before it trashes your kid…if it's not too late. Lord knows what your language is like at home—walls thickly painted with profanity.

Seven years old.

The father was under my skin, quickly becoming rancid and septic. And there they stood at my booth: the child lost in the imagery of my books, while the parents argued behind him with classy dad sporting the bold statement of the day.

I could not let this moment pass by without capturing it. While I would certainly relay to my friends what I had seen, it would take more than words to convey the full impact. So I took out my phone and discretely took a photo of the three. The father's shirt was clear as day.

*   *   *

The art festival was on the weekend. By noon the following Monday, I had shown the picture to nearly twenty people. "Want to see a photo of a kid who doesn't have a chance? Oh, and that's his dad behind him..."

Everyone's reaction was no different than mine: appalled and sad. For three days I continued to share the image and voice my opinion about the father. I lost sleep over the photo. I could not erase the four bold words printed on his shirt. I could not unsee it.

Then along came a conversation with a friend named Dianne...

"Ros, you know that photo you showed me earlier? It bothers you, doesn't it?"

I don't often admit to things that bother me, as I usually do a pretty good job of ignoring them. "Well," I said. "I wouldn't say I'm *bothered* so much as I'm just intrigued by the scene I captured."

"I understand that, "she said. "But you're showing it to everyone because it bothers you. Right?"

I hadn't shown it to Dianne with the hopes that she'd turn therapist on me. But it sure felt that way. "Okay, yes, it bothers me." *What was next? Hypnosis? Delve into my childhood? Interpret my dreams?*

"I'm going to give you some advice," she said. "Some Jim Pape wisdom."

Jim Pape was her late husband. He had passed away five years prior. A defense lawyer, Jim was well known for not only delivering great story jokes, but had a gift for putting things into perspective that often contained a valuable nugget of enduring wisdom.

"Obviously," she continued. "The child in that photo doesn't have much of a role model as a father. No doubt, the father's shirt is disgraceful. But think about this:

There is nothing you can do about the father. You'll never be able to change him."

"And that's the great wisdom you're passing on to me?"

Dianne let out a slight chuckle. "No, Ros. The wisdom is this: Chances are you'll never see him again. But as long as you keep showing that photo, and as long as you keep talking about it, well, that father will continue to live rent-free in your head."

"But, it's such a great photo. It captures everything."

"I get it, Ros. I get the dynamics of the photo. But my suggestion is to delete it. Let it go."

I couldn't argue with her. Living rent-free in my head was exactly what was going on. It was as if I'd granted the dad total access to every virtual square inch of my brain. He had become a fixation that I could not turn away from: in the grocery store, at a gas station, on a group run, or throughout my work day. It got to the point that if I wasn't showing the photo, then I was at least describing it.

Living rent-free, and the worst tenant possible. Dianne was right: there was nothing I could do to change a person who I'd never see again. I must admit though, he sure made for great conversation. Not one person sided with the dad. Nobody shared his choice for freedom of expression.

Still, how long did I want to continue parading the photo around town? How long would I lug this fixation around with me? By the end of the week, I made a decision to evict the tenant.

Heeding the wisdom of Jim Pape, I selected the photo from my phone one last time. I gazed into the innocent child's face mesmerized by my books. Such a pure and beautiful moment for him. I can only hope my books would be lasting memories.

And right there, before I pressed DELETE, I wished the child farewell.

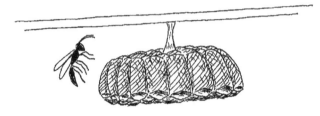

The Library

PART I
The Man In The Chair

He sat slumped in a cushioned chair in the library. One arm extended on the arm rest with the hand relaxed over the edge. The other hand, holding a tissue, was on his lap. Neck arched back—his head rested on top of the back cushion. His watery eyes, which stared directly at the ceiling, were looking *beyond* the ceiling. His physical being was in the library, but he was far removed.

I had come to work on a humorous story—to find a quiet, secluded spot to let my imagination run free. Funny how within the confines of your head, just how far a thought can travel. Most of the time you have complete control of its whereabouts, while other times a thought can wander off, but then reappear more inspiring than when it had left. I guess what intrigues me most about imagination—is the never knowing of how a thought ever arrived, and what creative path it will eventually take. But on this particular day, my imagination hit a road block. Humorous creativity wasn't flowing. Instead, I had found something else—a curiosity about the man in the chair.

At times he took deep breaths, followed by slow exhalations as he simultaneously closed his eyes. These were the moments he would lightly rock his head side to side. But for the majority of the time that I watched him, his eyes were open, fixated on something—something that only he could see. Perhaps something that he wished wasn't there—a regret, a mistake, or possibly a loss.

I wanted to lean towards him and say, "Whatever it is, it'll get better." I wanted to assure him that happier days lie ahead. I didn't know this man, but I wanted to guide him in a better direction.

I also didn't want to say a word. I didn't want to engage. I didn't want to make any eye contact. I wanted him to save himself. *Don't initiate. You know nothing about this man. He carries baggage you have no knowledge of. Write your humorous story, and stay distant.*

But the tears—the moist tissue in his hand—I could not ignore them. He was struggling. Back and forth, I weighed the pros and cons of whether or not to talk with him. *There's a story here. There's emotion. And there's a man in need.*

I've always said that anyone's deepest struggle is just one conversation away from being rescued. All I needed to do was reach out and give him a listening ear or some helpful words of advice. And if my advice might fall short of its intention, then at least I'd have given him some conversation, which, on its own, would be therapeutic.

For nearly an hour my mind travelled, running the gamut of just what possibly could be wrong. Oddly, it was almost as if I was getting to know him—that I was beginning to understand whatever it was I didn't know. Look at someone long enough, and sometimes you begin to wonder if, in fact, you've met that person before.

My time was up. I had to leave the library. I collected my belongings and made my way for the door. I had come to write a humorous story, but had written nothing. Instead, I walked away, only to be inspired by a thought a week later…

I wrote a story about a man I never talked to.

PART II
The Man In The Chair:
Discovered

In my last story, *The Man In The Chair*, I described my observations of a man who appeared to be troubled by something, but it was something I couldn't figure out. In the end, it was a man I never talked to. So I walked away, taking my assumptions with me.

It is now one week later, and, I must say, it's a beautiful thing when opportunity knocks twice…

I talked to the man in the chair.

I had gone to the library, again, to write a story. Much of my writing is done on my phone which makes it easy to write at any time or place. I settled into the same chair in which I had sat across from the man the week before. For ten minutes I paid no attention to my surroundings, but was simply immersed in writing. That is, until I looked up.

There he sat, across from me—the man from my story. And there I sat, surprised, staring at him and wondering what to do as he read a newspaper. I was hesitant to introduce myself. I knew nothing about this man. *What if I tell him I wrote a story and he takes offense? What if he makes a scene? What if he tells me to mind my own business?* I was *not* going to let this be a missed opportunity.

My focus had quickly slipped from my writing as I continued to take glances at the man. It was inevitable that I would say something. A few minutes passed before he got up to go to the magazine racks where he selected *Guitar*, then returned to his seat. *Hmmm…interesting…a musician. I mean who else looks at pages of musical notes? Good chance he plays the guitar, which means he enjoys the arts, which means there's a greater chance he'll like my story.* I waited for him to close the magazine before I spoke.

"Excuse me," I said. "But do you have a minute?"

"Sure," he replied.

"I'm a writer. I have a book coming out this year." I paused. There were so many different angles from which to start the conversation. "I really don't know where to begin." I paused a second time, then extended my hand. "I'm Ros."

"I'm John," he said, leaning forward to accept the handshake.

"I write about people. You sat there this past weekend staring at the ceiling. You caught my attention. I couldn't help but wonder what you were thinking. You seemed lost in thought. So I wrote this story."

I showed him my phone which was opened up to my writing blog site displaying the title, *The Man In The Chair.*

"That's you. I wrote about you."

Taken by surprise, he said, "You wrote about me?"

"Yes. It looked like you were dealing with something. Like a problem or a loss. I hope I'm not getting too personal, but something was obviously weighing on you."

Where a week ago I had walked away, never to know what was burdening him, I now had put him in a position to divulge his anguish.

John looked at me for just a moment, then chuckled. He pointed up through a large window next to where we sat. "See that wasp nest up there, under the eave? I was studying that. Watching them build."

Forget that I was in a library—a public sanctuary for silence. I just flat out laughed. "THAT!?" I said. "THAT was your problem? All the struggle I knew you were dealing with—something that was certainly wrenching deep inside you...and your 'problem' was that wasp nest!? This is just too funny."

How was it possible I was that far off the mark? I was certain he had made a poor decision, said a regretful comment, or had possibly suffered some kind of a loss. But, no. Far from it...

A wasp nest!

"Well, here it is if you're interested," I said, offering my phone to him so that he could read the story. "But please understand, it's an observational story based on my assumptions."

"No problem," he said, putting on a pair of reading glasses. "I'd like to read it."

For five minutes I watched John read—his expression changing from smiling to one of attentiveness. I couldn't help but wonder where his mind might be traveling. Here I was, a complete stranger, handing him a phone that contained a short story written specifically about him. He had every right to be weary of me—skeptical that I might have ulterior motives.

But when he finished reading and handed back my phone, it was clear he had cast aside whatever doubts he might have possessed regarding motives or just me in general.

As it turns out, there was something going on well beyond the wasp nest. John looked out the window toward the passing cars beyond the library's property. He began to reminisce and speak openly of his past and current state.

"Your story." He paused, as if collecting himself. Continuing to look out the window, he pointed blindly back at my phone. "Your story...it hit me." He took off his glasses and rubbed his eyes. He spoke softly with a peaceful demeanor. "You wrote that you wanted to tell me that things will get better, that happier days are ahead. You know, you could never have told me that one day I'd be homeless. That each night at the age of 65 I'd have to look for a patch of dirt or grass, or a slab of concrete to sleep on for the night. It's crazy. I mean I've had some incredible memories in my life."

I had to interject, and said, "Such as being a guitarist?"

"Actually, no." He said. "I was a drummer. Used to play with a group called 'Ronnie and the Sonics'. We opened for Willie Nelson at his 4th of July picnic concert in Applebee, Texas. Those were great times. Hell, a couple of our songs made the top charts list in Sweden of all places. It was pretty cool."

John paused, lightly shaking his head, then continued.

"You know, my mom always said that no matter what, things never stay the same. Everything changes. It doesn't mean they'll change for the better. Things can also change for the worse. So here I am, homeless. But I know one thing...you gotta believe in yourself to improve. Things don't just come to you."

The dynamics unfolds as I learn he used to be a welder. But he says if he could do it all over again he'd have been a chef, as he loves to cook. He has a son that lives in San Marcos and a daughter that lives in Austin. Due to the complexities of their situations, neither is in a position to help him out. His homeless condition has been going on for four months now. It was a sudden and unexpected reality when his landlord nearly tripled the rent on his mobile home. His only source of income is $900 from Social Security that is deposited into his bank account each month. All of his possessions are in a storage unit. I told him I'd keep my feelers out for any bargain rental spaces in town. But San Marcos being the fastest growing city in America, the likelihood of a "bargain" is slim.

At the end of our conversation, John said he wanted to go to Fredericksburg. "I hear there's a huge bat colony that flies out from an old gypsum mine each night in the summer. I'd love to see that. There's a $23 bus tour from here I can take. I'm gonna do it."

The man in the chair, like all of us, has a story. And he also has a name. I think there's a lot that John's going to do. I think he has enough ambition to find a way to a simple, but comfortable place to live. It may be a little bumpy getting there, but eventually he'll find his way. And it doesn't need to be much...just enough to be called Home.

The Remedy

It's not often that I come along and steal your attention, but I felt compelled. So I stole it in such a manner that whatever it was you were doing, was temporarily forgotten.

And there you were, on your little blue marble, with an ability to predict down to the second when, where, and how long I will occur at varying locations. The evolution of your science leading to such predictions is highly impressive.

I hope you saw something different as you looked through your viewing glasses. I hope you saw evidence that it's the simplest things that give you pleasure, such as being caught in wonderment of the apparent live chemistry of my shadows. And while you cautiously stayed clear of letting your naked eyes view the intensity of my dangerous light, you were completely drawn to my primal and short-lived beauty. So many laborers around your country shared their welding masks for others to safely stare upward into the darkening daylight sky. Some things just can't be passed up.

But I'm curious about something—your large corporations. Please tell me they stopped production to let your workers witness my presence. Please tell me they pulled the plug on their robots, conveyor belts, and assembly lines. For just a few minutes, is it possible they cared a little more about the alignment of two magnificent spheres in the sky and the lasting memories they would generate, and less about units sold per minute, and the revenue they would generate? Wishful thinking, I'm afraid.

I saw employees of small companies stepping outside. All of them exhibited the excitement of anticipation. There was clearly a difference in community between small and big businesses. Relationships in your smaller companies demonstrated a more cohesive atmosphere, whereas the larger a company's workforce, then, exponentially, the greater was the disconnect between employees.

From my perspective, it was truly the relationships between your people that caught my attention. As you were looking at me, I was looking at you. And, oh, the wonderful things I saw. There was sharing, smiling, and, for many, the giddiness of witnessing something new. All it took was a darkened lens to look through, and millions of your people were suddenly united.

And to think that I had the ability to make an impact on people— that my infrequent occurrence touched lives. In particular, two people stood out most: A therapist and his client. It was a dire situation in which the client was suffering. His bloodshot eyes welled with despair. His life burdened with depression.

"Take hold of yourself, John," said the therapist. "This will all pass. You just have to accept that, and let time do its healing."

"But, I had no idea the fallout. I had no idea the repercussions," John replied with his hands trembling as he then buried his face within them.

The therapist was without words. He had counseled as best he could. John's rebound truly was at the mercy of time. But time did not always comply fast enough. Pain and suffering lingered in the tedium of time's relentlessly slow pace. Especially in the dark insomniac hours of sleeplessness.

Dark, thought the therapist. *Dark!*

"John," he said, looking at his watch. "We're not too late!"

"For what?"

He stood up and helped John out of his seat. "Come with me. You need to see this."

"See what?"

"Your remedy, John. Your remedy."

As they made their way outside, the therapist grabbed two pairs of viewing glasses from a nearby table. "Here," he said, handing one to John. "Put these on, then look up at the sun. I'll do the same."

Less than a minute later they were standing in a parking lot, looking at me in awe. And for the first time in who knows how long, a smile widened across John's face. "It's beautiful," he said. "Absolutely beautiful."

"Keep looking at it, John," said the therapist. "Take it all in. Total eclipses are not only rare, but pass quickly."

"It's stunning," said John. "This is just incredible. I've been so locked up inside my head lately...well, for quite some time, that I've lost touch with my surroundings. I had no idea the eclipse was coming. I've been buried in the dark."

The therapist smiled. "It's funny...the potential of darkness, and the effect it can have on us. Here we stand in its shadow as it steals our light, and we welcome it with unanimous approval."

"I don't know how to explain it," said John, "But I do suddenly feel better. I feel *lifted*, if that makes any sense. Like I've gained some sort of clarity."

"It makes all the sense in the world, John. Perfect sense."

It wasn't long after, as daylight returned and darkness faded, that my time came to an end. And in my parting minutes I had the privilege to watch John do something that I'm sure he never saw coming...

Holding onto that smile, he continued to look up at me. And in a moment of newfound clarity, he took a deep breath, and then silently mouthed the words, "Thank you."

CPSIA information can be obtained
at www.ICGtesting.com
Printed in the USA
BVHW071242191218
535965BV00004B/290/P

9 781596 875272